ENGLISH

Communication Skills in the New Millennium

Y0-CDJ-502

ESL Practice and
Test Preparation

Level I

Educating tomorrow today.

BARRETT KENDALL PUBLISHING

AUSTIN, TEXAS

Photo Credits

Key: (t) top, (c) center, (b) bottom, (l) left, (r) right.

Page 16, Bettmann/Corbis; 23, Bettmann/Corbis;
30, Diego Lezama Orezzoli/Corbis; 37, Andrea Booher/
Tony Stone Images; 44, Corbis; 51, William A. Bake/
Corbis; 58, Reuters NewMedia Inc./Corbis; 65, Felicia
Martinez/PhotoEdit; 72, Peter Johnson/Corbis;
79, David Austen/Stock Boston; 91, S. Krulwich/NYT
Pictures; 93, Mary Kate Denny/PhotoEdit; 96, Bob
Daemmrich Photography; 99, David Young-Wolff/Tony
Stone Images; 102, David Young-Wolff/PhotoEdit;
105, David Young-Wolff/PhotoEdit; 108, Jane Tyska/
Stock Boston; 111, David Young-Wolff/PhotoEdit;
114, Chip Henderson/Tony Stone Images; 117, Spencer
Grant/PhotoEdit; 120, Michael Newman/PhotoEdit;
123, Francisco Cruz/SuperStock; 126, David Young-
Wolff/PhotoEdit; 129, Mary Kate Denny/PhotoEdit;
132, Michael Newman/PhotoEdit; 135, Jeff Greenberg
/PhotoEdit; 138, Jeff Greenberg/PhotoEdit;
141, GrantPix/Stock Boston; 144(t), George Lepp/
Corbis; 144(b), Jim Zuckerman/Corbis; 148, Rex
Rystedt/Tony Stone; 152(t), Bettmann/Corbis;
152(b), Morton Beebe, SF/Corbis; 156, F.M. Cox/Stock
Boston; 160(t), Hulton Getty Collection; 160(bl), Hulton-
Deutsch Collection/Corbis; 160(br), Underwood &
Underwood/Corbis; 164, Bettmann/Corbis; 168, Lester
Lefkowirz/The Stock Market; 172, Bettmann/Corbis.

ISBN 1-58079-351-7

1 2 3 4 5 6 7   HG   06 05 04 03 02 01

One of the biggest challenges facing the Grade 9 English teacher is how to include those students who are still acquiring English. English language learners may be at many different levels of English proficiency, and the challenge is often to include them without impeding the instruction of native speakers. *BK English ESL Practice and Test Preparation* has been designed to help you provide additional, focused practice, based on the *BK English* Pupil Edition, for English language learners. The practice can help you bring those students into the mainstream, whether they are at basic, intermediate, or advanced levels of English proficiency.

In addition to the practice pages related to chapters in the Composition and Language sections of the Pupil Edition, this book contains ESL lessons for the first eight units in *BK English Standardized Test Preparation*. ESL students are required to take the same standardized tests that are taken by native English speakers. The practice in this book will help prepare English language learners both for the later units of Standardized Test Preparation as well as the test itself.

The **Composition** section includes an excerpt from the chapter reading selection in BK English, with comprehension questions and skills activities for each level of proficiency. In addition there is a writing prompt based on the writing assignment at the end of the chapter in the Pupil's Edition. A graphic organizer is included to assist ESL students in their writing.

The **Language** section contains a reading passage about a real-life situation. Practice of chapter skills is followed by tactile and oral activities related to the reading that will engage the student in using the relevant language skills.

The **Test Preparation** section, corresponding to the first eight units of *BK English Standardized Test Preparation*, consists of four parts: a reading passage with guided reading questions to help student comprehension, three multiple choice questions focused on reading skills, a guided writing prompt that includes a graphic organizer, and a passage for students to edit for grammar, usage, or mechanics.

Table of Contents

▷ **COMPOSITION**

Chapter 1: Using Your Writing Process
Guided Reading 1
Developing Your Skills
   Recognizing Fact and Opinion: *Basic* 2–3
   Recognizing Facts: *Intermediate* 4
   Supporting with Facts: *Advanced* 5

Chapter 2: Developing Your Writing Style
Guided Reading 6
Developing Your Skills
   Identifying Supporting Details: *Basic* 7–8
   Identifying Supporting Details: *Intermediate* . . . 9
   Providing Supporting Details: *Advanced* 10

Chapter 3: Writing Informative Paragraphs
Guided Reading 11
Developing Your Skills
   Using the Correct Word: *Basic* 12–13
   Using the Correct Word: *Intermediate* 14
   Using Vivid Words: *Advanced* 15
Process of Writing 16–17

Chapter 4: Writing Well-Structured Paragraphs
Guided Reading 18
Developing Your Skills
   Transition Words: *Basic* 19–20
   Point of View: *Intermediate* 21
   Descriptive Paragraphs: *Advanced* 22
Process of Writing 23–24

Chapter 5: Writing Effective Compositions
Guided Reading 25
Developing Your Skills
   Determining the Meanings of Words: *Basic* . . 26–27
   Determining Word Meanings: *Intermediate* 28
   Determining the Meanings
     of Words: *Advanced* 29
Process of Writing 30–31

Chapter 6: Writing Effective Compositions
Guided Reading 32
Developing Your Skills
   Descriptive, Sensory and
     Background Details: *Basic* 33–34
   Creating Vivid Images: *Intermediate* 35
   Writing Vivid Details: *Advanced* 36
Process of Writing 37–38

Chapter 7: Using Description: Observation
Guided Reading 39
Developing Your Skills
   Descriptive Writing: *Basic* 40–41
   Using Figurative Language: *Intermediate* 42
   Writing Descriptions Using
     Figurative Language: *Advanced* 43
Process of Writing 44–45

Chapter 8: Creative Writing: Stories, Plays, and Poems
Guided Reading 46
Developing Your Skills
   Descriptive Topic Sentences: *Basic* 47–48
   Ordering Events: *Intermediate* 49
   Choosing Character Traits: *Advanced* 50
Process of Writing 51–52

Chapter 9: Writing to Inform and Explain
Guided Reading 53
Developing Your Skills
   Types of Order: *Basic* 54–55
   Types of Order: *Intermediate* 56
   Writing Sentences Using Pronouns: *Advanced* . . . 57
Process of Writing 58–59

Chapter 10: Writing to Persuade
Guided Reading 60
Developing Your Skills
   Identifying Your Audience: *Basic* 61–62
   Identifying Your Audience: *Intermediate* 63
   Writing Topic Sentences: *Advanced* 64
Process of Writing 65–66

Chapter 11: Writing About Literature
Guided Reading 67
Developing Your Skills
   Gathering Evidence: *Basic* 68–69
   Gathering Evidence: *Intermediate* 70
   Gathering Evidence: *Advanced* 71
Process of Writing 72–73

Chapter 12: Research Reports
Guided Reading 74
Developing Your Skills
   Choosing and Limiting a Research
     Subject: *Basic* 75–76
   Works Cited Page: *Intermediate* 77
   Limiting a Research Subject and
     Developing a Thesis: *Advanced* 78
Process of Writing 79–80

Chapter 13: Letters and Applications
Guided Reading 81
Developing Your Skills
  Writing Letters: *Basic* 82–83
  Business Letters: *Intermediate* 84
  Writing Letters: *Advanced* 85

Chapter 14: Speeches, Presentations and Discussions
Guided Reading 86
Developing Your Skills
  Choosing and Limiting a Subject: *Basic* 87–88
  Strategies for Listening—
    Recognizing Appeals: *Intermediate* 89
  Strategies for Listening—
    Glittering Generalities: *Advanced* 90
Process of Writing 91–92

▷ LANGUAGE

Chapter 1: The Sentence
Real-Life Language 93–94
A Different Approach 95

Chapter 2: Nouns and Pronouns
Real-Life Language 96–97
A Different Approach 98

Chapter 3: Verbs
Real-Life Language 99–100
A Different Approach 101

Chapter 4: Adjectives and Adverbs
Real-Life Language 102–103
A Different Approach 104

Chapter 5: Other Parts of Speech
Real-Life Language 105–106
A Different Approach 107

Chapter 6: Complements
Real-Life Language 108–109
A Different Approach 110

Chapter 7: Phrases
Real-Life Language 111–112
A Different Approach 113

Chapter 8: Clauses
Real-Life Language 114–115
A Different Approach 116

Chapter 9: Sentence Fragments and Run-ons
Real-Life Language 117–118
A Different Approach 119

Chapter 10: Using Verbs
Real-Life Language 120–121
A Different Approach 122

Chapter 11: Using Pronouns
Real-Life Language 123–124
A Different Approach 125

Chapter 12: Subject and Verb Agreement
Real-Life Language 126–127
A Different Approach 128

Chapter 13: Using Adjectives and Adverbs
Real-Life Language 129–130
A Different Approach 131

Chapter 14: Capital Letters
Real-Life Language 132–133
A Different Approach 134

Chapter 15: End Marks and Commas
Real-Life Language 135–136
A Different Approach 137

Chapter 16: Italics and Quotation Marks
Real-Life Language 138–139
A Different Approach 140

Chapter 17: Other Punctuation
Real-Life Language 141–142
A Different Approach 14

▷ TEST PREPARATION

Unit 1: What to Do If You See a Bear
Reading 144–145
Composition 146
Editing 147

Unit 2: Sherman Alexie's "This is What it Means to Say Phoenix, Arizona"
Reading 148–149
Composition 150
Editing 151

Unit 3: When Squids Attack
Reading 152–153
Composition 154

Editing 155

Unit 4: You Call This a Vacation?
Reading 156–157
Composition 158
Editing 159

**Unit 5: *Fortitudine Vincimus*—
        By Endurance We Conquer**
Reading 160–161
Composition 162
Editing 163

**Unit 6: Sports Heroes Deserve High Salaries;
        What's Up With Sports Salaries?**
Reading 164–165
Composition 166
Editing 167

Unit 7: New York, New York
Reading 168–169
Composition 170
Editing 171

Unit 8: An American Original
Reading 172–173
Composition 174
Editing 175

▷ **ANSWER KEY** 176

USING YOUR WRITING PROCESS CHAPTER 1

▷ GUIDED READING

Read the passage and answer the questions that follow.

"Straw into Gold," FROM *The Metamorphosis of the Everyday,* by Sandra Cisneros

I've managed to do a lot of things in my life I didn't think I was <u>capable</u> of and of which many others didn't think me capable either. **[1]**

Especially because I'm a woman, a Latina, an only daughter in a family of six men. My father would've liked to have seen me married long ago. In our culture, men and women don't leave their father's house except by way of marriage. I crossed my father's threshold with nothing carrying me but my own two feet. A woman whom no one came for and no one chased away . . . **[2]**

I like to think that somehow my family, my Mexicanness, my poverty all had something to do with shaping me into a writer. I like to think my parents were <u>preparing</u> me all along for my life as an artist even though they didn't know it. From my father I <u>inherited</u> a love of wandering. He was born in Mexico City but as a young man he traveled to the U.S. vagabonding. He eventually was drafted and thus became a citizen. From him I inherited a <u>sappy</u> heart. (He still cries when he watches the Mexican soaps—especially if they deal with children who have <u>forsaken</u> their parents.) **[3]**

My mother was born like me—in Chicago but of Mexican descent . . . It would be her tough, streetwise voice that would haunt all of my stories and poems . . .

Guided Reading

1. How does the writer grab your attention?
2. How do these details support the statement above?
3. How has your family shaped you?

VOCABULARY

capable: able
preparing: making ready
inherited: received
sappy: sentimental
forsaken: abandoned

READING COMPREHENSION

_____ **1.** What is the main idea of the second paragraph?
  A The author is unusual in her culture because she left home without getting married.
  B The author's parents expected her to have a career.
  C The author always wanted to get married.
  D The author has a lot of brothers.

_____ **2.** Which of the following did the author NOT inherit from her father?
  A A love of travel
  B A sappy heart
  C Mexicanness
  D A love of fine cuisine

Chapter 1 Using Your Writing Process • Level I COMPOSITION   **1**

Copyright © Barrett Kendall Publishing. All rights reserved.

RECOGNIZING FACT AND OPINION   A fact is something that is true. An opinion expresses what a writer thinks or believes. Opinions often use words like *must, ought* and *should*. For each statement below, choose A if it is a fact or B if it is an opinion.

COMPOSITION

_____ **1.** Sandra Cisneros wrote "Straw into Gold."
   A fact
   B opinion

_____ **2.** Cisneros' writes that her family had something to do with shaping her as a writer.
   A fact
   B opinion

_____ **3.** Cisneros father became a U.S. citizen because he was drafted.
   A fact
   B opinion

_____ **4.** Cisneros should win many awards for her writing.
   A fact
   B opinion

_____ **5.** Cisneros got her sentimental side from her father.
   A fact
   B opinion

_____ **6.** Cisneros' mother must be proud of her.
   A fact
   B opinion

_____ **7.** Cisneros' mother is tough.
   A fact
   B opinion

_____ **8.** All people ought to respect their parents.
   A fact
   B opinion

_____ **9.** In "Straw into Gold" Cisneros writes about her family.
   A fact
   B opinion

_____**10.** All writers should write about their families.
   A fact
   B opinion

DEVELOPING YOUR SKILLS

CLARIFYING IDEAS Imagine that you are going to write an essay about your family. Using the graphic above, respond to the following phrases, writing what you think in the "what you think" circle and what your parents think in the "what my parents think" circle. If you think the same way about something as your parents, write it in the middle, where the circles overlap.

1. About marriage
2. About working
3. About travel
4. About art
5. About education

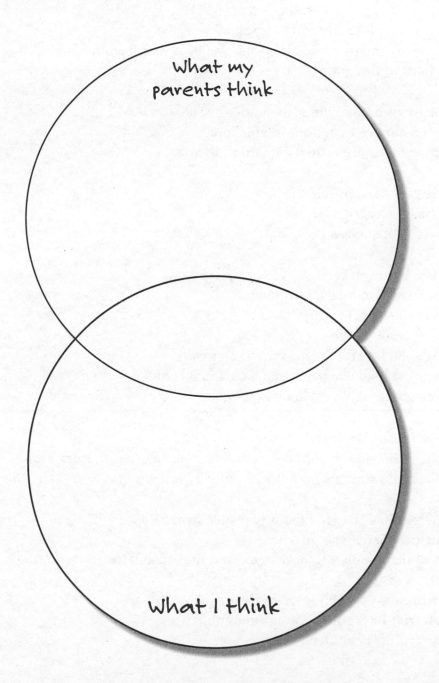

DEVELOPING YOUR SKILLS
....

RECOGNIZING FACTS Specific facts help to support and explain
opinions. In the sentences below, choose the statement that best
supports each opinion.

INTERMEDIATE

_____ **1.** Mexico City is the largest city in Mexico.
   A It has a population of over 8 million people.
   B Millions of people live there.

_____ **2.** Education is important to Americans.
   A Many Americans are educated.
   B The U.S. government provides free public education.

_____ **3.** It can be difficult to support yourself as an artist.
   A The average artist makes less than $5,000 a year from her art.
   B It is hard to find jobs for artists.

_____ **4.** Organic foods are healthier than non-organic foods.
   A They cost more than non-organic foods.
   B Organic foods are grown without pesticides.

_____ **5.** Maria is well-liked at school.
   A She has many friends.
   B She was voted class President.

_____ **6.** David is a hard worker.
   A He worked two jobs all summer.
   B He says he likes to work.

_____ **7.** Cooking school makes someone a better cook.
   A Cooking school teaches specific cooking techniques.
   B Cooking school offers many experiences.

_____ **8.** Public radio stations need money.
   A Public radio stations often have fund-drives in order to raise money.
   B Public radio stations are under-funded.

_____ **9.** The internet has changed the way people work.
   A Many people use the internet.
   B 30% of the population now "telecommutes" using the internet.

_____ **10.** Fresh fruit makes a better snack than cookies.
   A Fresh fruit has more vitamins and minerals.
   B Fresh fruit is healthier.

▶ DEVELOPING YOUR SKILLS

SUPPORTING WITH FACTS   Each pair of sentences gives facts about a topic. Read the facts. Then write an opinion based on the facts.

1. When eaten together, rice and beans form a complete protein.
   Protein is an important part of a balanced diet.

   OPINION: _____

   _____

2. Oil and coal are energy sources that are not renewable.
   Renewable energy sources are important to our future.

   OPINION: _____

   _____

3. The Olympics happen every four years.
   Some athletes are too young to qualify for the Olympics.

   OPINION: _____

   _____

4. Tomatoes are fruit.
   Tomatoes are a good source of vitamin C.

   OPINION: _____

   _____

5. Caffeine can keep people awake at night.
   Warm milk can cause people to feel sleepy.

   OPINION: _____

   _____

VOCABULARY

writing process: steps you take in order to express your ideas

portfolio: a collection of your writing work

freewriting: writing without stopping about whatever comes to mind

journal: a notebook where you write down your thoughts and ideas

purpose: what you want to accomplish with your writing

occasion: why you are writing

audience: who you are writing for

supporting details: facts, examples and reasons that back up your ideas

brainstorming: thinking of all the things that a topic brings to mind

classifying: grouping items into categories

COMPOSITION

COMPOSITION

▷ GUIDED READING

Read the passage and answer the questions that follow.

FROM *I Know Why the Caged Bird Sings,*
by Maya Angelou

Mrs. Bertha Flowers was the <u>aristocrat</u> of Black Stamps. She had the grace of control to appear warm in the coldest weather, and on the Arkansas summer days it seemed she had a private breeze which <u>swirled</u> around, cooling her. **[1]**

She said, without turning her head, to me, "I hear you're doing very good school work, Marguerite, but that it's all written. The teachers report that they have trouble getting you to talk in class."

"Now no one is going to make you talk—possibly no one can. But <u>bear</u> in mind, language is man's way of communicating with his fellow man and it is language alone which <u>separates</u> him from the lower animals." **[2]** That was a totally new idea to me, and I would need time to think about it.

"Your grandmother says you read a lot. Every chance you get. That's good, but not good enough. Words mean more than what is set down on paper. It takes the human voice to <u>infuse</u> them with the shades of deeper meaning." **[3]**

I <u>memorized</u> the part about the human voice infusing words. It seemed so <u>valid</u> and poetic. She said she was going to give me some books and that I not only must read them, I must read them aloud. She suggested that I try to make a sentence sound in as many different ways as possible . . .

Guided Reading

1. How is Mrs. Flowers different from other residents of Black Stamps?

2. What is she saying here about language?

3. What detail does Maya Angelou give to show how spoken language is different than writing?

VOCABULARY

aristocrat: upper class
swirled: move in a twisting motion
bear: keep
separates: sets apart
infuse: fill
memorized: learned by heart
valid: well grounded

READING COMPREHENSION

_____ **1.** What is the main idea of the passage?
  A Speaking is important.
  B Staying cool in summer is not easy.
  C Writing is the same as speaking.
  D Aristocrats offer good advice.

_____ **2.** Based on the passage, what is Maya Angelou's point of view regarding speaking?
  A That it is good, but not important.
  B That it necessary.
  C That it is less important than writing.
  D That it is a waste of time.

DEVELOPING YOUR SKILLS

IDENTIFYING SUPPORTING DETAILS   **Supporting details help back up an idea or opinion. For each of the sentences below, pick *yes* if the second sentence supports the first or *no* if it does not.**

_____ **1.** Reading out loud is important to Mrs. Flowers. She believes the human voice infuses words with meaning.
 A yes
 B no

_____ **2.** Marguerite enjoyed eating the cookies Mrs. Flowers made. She liked to read too.
 A yes
 B no

_____ **3.** Marguerite did not like to talk in school. Her teachers had a difficult time getting her to speak in class.
 A yes
 B no

_____ **4.** Mrs. Flowers is the aristocrat of Black Stamps. She carries herself with distinction.
 A yes
 B no

_____ **5.** Mrs. Flowers made cookies in the morning. The sweet scent of vanilla lingered in her home.
 A yes
 B no

_____ **6.** The lemonade is in the ice-box. The cookies are delicious.
 A yes
 B no

_____ **7.** Marguerite loves to read. She reads a book a day.
 A yes
 B no

_____ **8.** Her brother is funny. He plays basketball for the school.
 A yes
 B no

_____ **9.** My parents are strict. They work in an office.
 A yes
 B no

_____ **10.** Reading aloud is fun. My sister and I read instead of watching TV.
 A yes
 B no

COMPOSITION

CLUSTERING   Imagine that you are going to write an essay about an opinion or idea that you have about the following topics. In the center of the diagram, write the opinion. In the outer circles, write details that support your idea. Complete this exercise on a separate sheet of paper.

COMPOSITION

1. Reading

2. School work

3. Your family

4. Your home

5. Your best friend

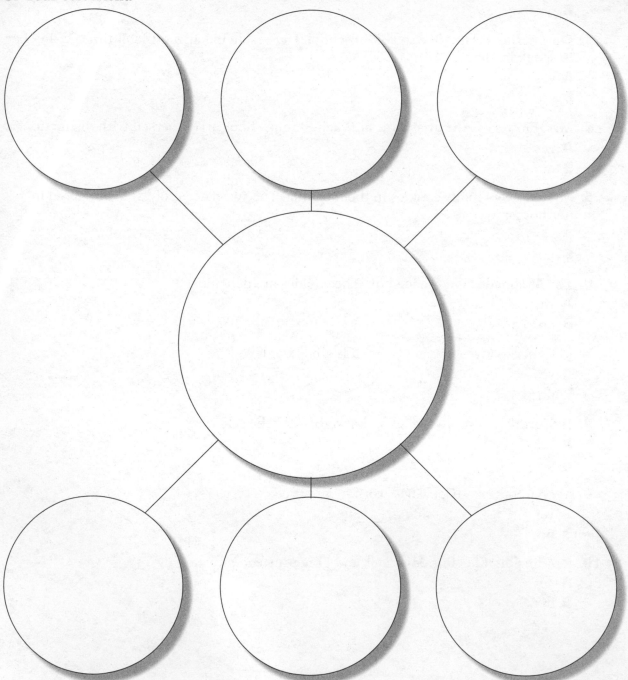

▶ DEVELOPING YOUR SKILLS

IDENTIFYING SUPPORTING DETAILS   Supporting details are
facts, examples or beliefs that back up an idea. A supporting detail helps
explain a statement or idea. Choose the detail which best supports the
idea of each of the following statements.

____ **1.** Language separates humans from animals.
    A Humans are the only creatures with written language.
    B Many people speak two languages.

____ **2.** Words take on deeper shades of meaning when spoken aloud.
    A I could tell she was excited from the way she read her speech.
    B Words can be confusing.

____ **3.** Reading out loud can gives a new meaning to a book or poem.
    A It reminds people of when they were young.
    B It helps reveal the music of the language.

____ **4.** That movie was really funny.
    A I laughed the entire time.
    B It was two hours long.

____ **5.** Reading opens up new worlds.
    A I like to read.
    B I feel like I've been to China after reading that book.

____ **6.** Sitting in front of the computer for too long can tire your eyes.
    A Everyone seems to have a computer.
    B My vision is blurry after playing that computer game for hours.

____ **7.** Good manners are important.
    A I liked him because he said "please" and "thank you."
    B He didn't make much of an impression.

____ **8.** People should vote.
    A The bill for school funding passed by two votes.
    B The election was held on a Tuesday.

____ **9.** Dogs are loyal.
    A My dog waited for me all day.
    B My dog can do tricks.

____ **10.** Scooters are fun.
    A He rode his scooter all afternoon.
    B His scooter is silver.

PROVIDING SUPPORTING DETAILS   **For each of sentence below,**   ADVANCED
write two supporting details.

1. Mary loves to read fiction.

_____

_____

_____

2. Her house is cold in the winter.

_____

_____

_____

3. Lance is a good writer.

_____

_____

_____

4. Mia is great at math.

_____

_____

_____

5. Tadashi is a good actor.

_____

_____

_____

VOCABULARY

style: how you express yourself

figurative language: words that paint pictures in your reader's mind

similes: comparisons using *like* or *as*

metaphor: a comparison where you say one thing *is* another

cliché: comparisons that are overused

coordinating conjunction: a word that links ideas of equal importance

common noun: any person, place or thing

proper noun: a particular person, place or thing

GUIDED READING

Read the passage and answer the questions that follow.

FROM *The Life and Death of a Western Gladiator,*
by Charles G. Finney

His very smallness at birth protected him when he most needed protection. <u>Instinct</u> provided him with what he lacked in experience. **[1]** In order to eat he first had to kill, and he was <u>eminently</u> adapted for killing. In sacs in his jaws he secreted a <u>virulent</u> poison. To inject that poison he had two fangs, hollow and pointed. Without that poison and those fangs he would have been among the most helpless creatures on earth. With them he was among the deadliest.

He was, of course, a baby rattlesnake, a desert diamondback, named *Crotalus attox* . . .

On the fourth day of his life he decided to go out into the world himself. He rippled forth uncertainly, the transverse plates on his belly serving him as legs.

He could see things well enough within his limited range . . . He had an excellent sense of smell. But, having no ears, he was stone deaf. On the other hand, he had a pit, a deep pock mark between eye and nostril. <u>Unique</u>, this organ was sensitive to animal heat. **[2]** In <u>pitch</u> blackness, Crotalus, by means of the heat messages recorded in his pit, could tell whether another animal was near and could also judge its size. . . .

He came upon a baby lizard. . . . Eyes, nose, pit, and tongue told Crotalus it was there. **[3]** Instinct told him what it was and what to do.

Guided Reading

1. What enables the snake able to survive?

2. What does this detail show?

3. What do you think the snake is going to do?

VOCABULARY

instinct: inborn motivation
eminently: highly
virulent: deadly
unique: special
pitch: extremely dark

READING COMPREHENSION

_____ **1.** What is the main idea of the third paragraph?

    A Snakes are creepy.

    B Snakes have many features that help them to survive.

    C Rattlesnakes are poisonous.

    D Snakes cannot tolerate cold climates.

_____ **2.** Which of the following is an opinion?

    A He rippled forth uncertainly.

    B If the temperature dropped too low he would freeze.

    C He had a pit, a deep pock mark between eye and nostril.

    D Without food he would starve.

▶ DEVELOPING YOUR SKILLS

USING THE CORRECT WORD Each of the following sentences is missing a word. If the word at the end of each sentence makes sense in the sentence, pick *yes*, if it does not, pick *no*.

____ **1.** A baby rattlesnake ■ five inches long. is
   A yes
   B no

____ **..** A rattlesnake's fangs ■ hollow. is
   A yes
   B no

____ **3.** Some snake dens have as ■ as two hundred snakes in them. many
   A yes
   B no

____ **4.** A grown rattlesnake snake is one of the ■ creatures on earth. deadliest
   A yes
   B no

____ **5.** A snake's tongue is ■ an exposed nerve. like
   A yes
   B no

____ **6.** When a snake sheds its skin, its eyes ■ over until it cannot see. cloud
   A yes
   B no

____ **7.** A twenty-year old ■ can be up to twenty feet long. rattlesnake
   A yes
   B no

____ **8.** Snakes ■ an excellent sense of smell. has
   A yes
   B no

____ **9.** Snakes ■ stone deaf. is
   A yes
   B no

____ **10.** Snakes have a pit that helps them ■ the heat of other animals. sense
   A yes
   B no

▶ DEVELOPING YOUR SKILLS

WORD WEB Imagine that you are going to write a story about a baby snake. Use the following list to help you generate vivid and interesting words to describe the snake. In the center of the diagram, write a word from the list. In the outer circles, write as many words or ideas that come to mind. Make a diagram for each word on a separate sheet of paper.

1. heat
2. cave
3. poisonous
4. rattlers
5. instinct

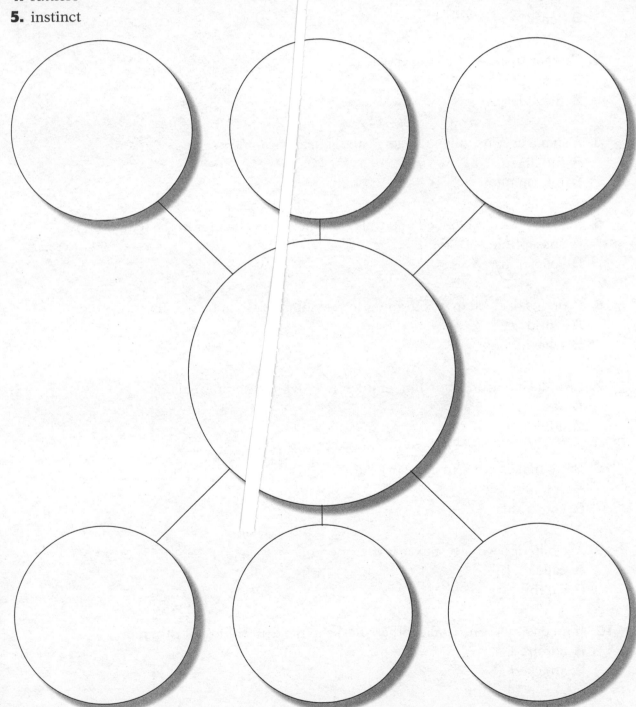

USING THE CORRECT WORD   Choose the answer that
completes each sentence.

COMPOSITION

____ **1.** Snakes are ■ creatures that never share food.
   A solitary
   B social

____ **2.** In pitch blackness a snake can use its pit to ■ the heat of another animal.
   A see
   B sense

____ **3.** Hunger ■ snakes to leave the den.
   A motivates
   B meanders

____ **4.** A snake uses its tongue to get ■ about its environment.
   A intelligent
   B information

____ **5.** Snakes are cold-blooded and thus extremely ■ to changes in the temperature.
   A susceptible
   B suspicious

____ **6.** Crotalus decided to go out into the ■ by himself when he was four days old.
   A world
   B whereabouts

____ **7.** Crotalus's poison made him eminently ■ to kill other animals.
   A able
   B addled

____ **8.** Baby snakes are ■ to large predators.
   A volatile
   B vulnerable

____ **9.** A group of newborn snakes is ■ a litter.
   A called
   B careful

____**10.** If an enemy ■ one snake, other snakes in the den would not respond.
   A admired
   B attacked

▷ DEVELOPING YOUR SKILLS

USING VIVID WORDS   **Each of the following sentences contains an underlined cliché. Revise each sentence using words that are more vivid and imaginative.**

1. John turned <u>white as a sheet</u> when he saw the giant rattlesnake lying in his path.

_____

_____

2. The snake lay there and, <u>cool as a cucumber</u>, stared at John.

_____

_____

3. Roberta <u>ate like a bird</u>.

_____

_____

4. Rochelle exclaimed, "You nearly <u>scared me to death</u>!"

_____

_____

5. Finding my keys is like <u>searching for a needle in a haystack</u>.

_____

_____

PROCESS OF WRITING AN INFORMATIVE PARAGRAPH

COMPOSITION

VOCABULARY

topic sentence: states the main idea of a paragraph

supporting sentences: explain the topic sentence

informative writing: explains or informs

analyzing: breaking down a whole into its parts

sequential order: arranges details in the order in which events take place

chronological order: arranges details in the order in which events occur over time

spatial order: arranges details according to their location

body of the paragraph: all of the supporting sentences

cause and effect: why actions or situations produce certain results

how-to paragraph: step-by-step instructions

A Writer Writes (pages C147–C148)

Purpose: to explain a behavior or characteristic
Audience: younger students

BASIC/INTERMEDIATE

Write a paragraph describing something from nature. Think about a characteristic that interests you, like why jellyfish glow in the dark or how Venus flytraps catch flies. Then brainstorm a list of details that you know about your topic. Use the Internet or your science book for ideas and information. When you have all of your details listed, draft your paragraph.

Purpose: to explain a behavior or characteristic
Audience: younger students

ADVANCED

Write a paragraph describing something from nature. Think about a characteristic that interests you, like why jellyfish glow in the dark or how Venus flytraps catch flies. Brainstorm a list of details that you know about your topic. Then brainstorm a list of why you think it is interesting. Use the Internet or your science book for ideas and information. When you have all of your details listed, draft your paragraph. Be sure to include reasons why the characteristic is interesting as well as a description of the characteristic.

16 Chapter 3 Writing Informative Paragraphs • Level I COMPOSITION

PROCESS OF WRITING AN INFORMATIVE PARAGRAPH

1. What do you like about your topic? Make a list.

2. From all of the items on your list, pick the top three. Use just these for your paragraph.

3. Use the diagram below to help you organize your ideas. State your opinion or topic sentence, then list your reasons that support it. Write a conclusion that sums up your ideas.

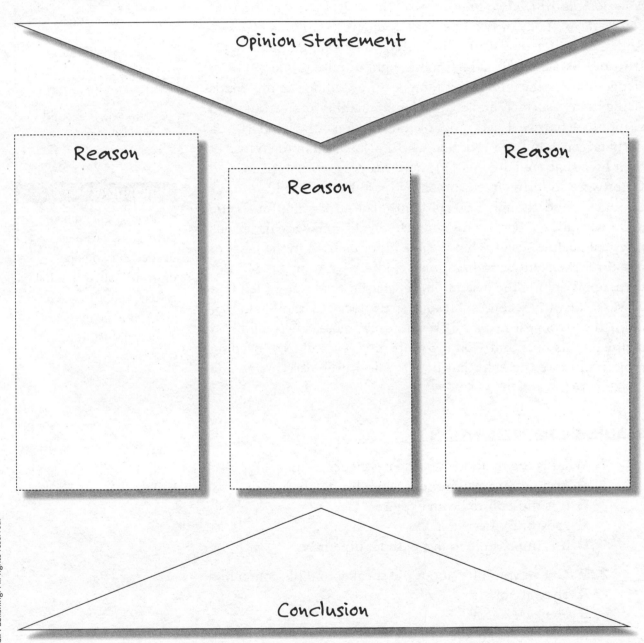

COMPOSITION

GUIDED READING

Read the passage and answer the questions that follow.

FROM *A Flag at the Pole*, by Paxton Davis

Will it show we knew ourselves doomed? [1] For though the likelihood of our dying was at that moment a thought still unspoken, to my journal, to myself, I admitted my apprehension: *Now for the run home and a desperate struggle. I wonder if we can do it.* As, a day or two later: *I'm afraid we are in for a bad pull.* And, a day after that: *Things beginning to look a little serious.* [2] It would be, as all of us knew, and eight-hundred-mile job of it, sledge-hauling the entire way, temperatures falling rapidly, winds rising, snow surface at its most unpredictably dangerous, and without—what we'd had most of the way out—the support of a party larger than five tired men who'd just stared in the refuse of their own shattered dreams. [3] *I don't like the look of it.* Evans and Oates were suffering from spreading frostbite, Wilson from snow blindness; and though Bowers continued strong and energetic and I was myself, despite my seniority in age, unaware of serious physical decline, I saw what lay ahead for us both in the faces of our three weakening companions. Still . . . we went on. . . . But then, approaching the decent of the Glacier, Evans and I fell into crevasses, Evan's second such spill; and afterward, though to that point the strongest of us all, Evan's grew increasingly dull and confused, his cuts and wounds reopening, eyes glazed, needing more and more the help that till then he'd been able to give the rest. . . . [4]

Guided Reading

1. What important information does the author include in the first sentence?

2. Why does the author include these thoughts?

3. What do these details show?

4. What do you think will happen?

VOCABULARY

doomed: condemned
apprehension: fear
desperate: no hope
unpredictably: unreliably
refuse: rubbish
glacier: huge mass of snow on land
crevasses: deep cracks

READING COMPREHENSION

_____ 1. What is the main idea of the passage?
  A An Anarctic explorer describes his death.
  B It is difficult to be an explorer.
  C Frostbite can be deadly.
  D It is impossible to live without dreams.

_____ 2. What can you infer about the speaker and his companions?
  A They are brave.
  B They are angry.
  C They are excited.
  D They are irritable.

DEVELOPING YOUR SKILLS

TRANSITION WORDS   **Select the sentence that includes transition words that show the order in which events occur.**

_____ **1. A** I saw something flashing in the distance.
       B It was then that I began to feel better.

_____ **2. A** I shouted with joy.
       B At first I thought our journey was over.

_____ **3. A** Meanwhile, Jacob has lost his way.
       B He had stopped to rest.

_____ **4. A** Jacob took a break when he found a good rock to sit on.
       B I wasn't feeling very tired because I wanted to go home.

_____ **5. A** I didn't know where to look for Jacob.
       B Suddenly I was aware that our journey would last longer.

_____ **6. A** I shouted his name, but after a while I walked back down the path.
       B I looked into the woods, but I didn't see him anywhere.

_____ **7. A** After ten minutes I started to get tired and sat on a rock.
       B I called out his name from where I was sitting.

_____ **8. A** I sat there and wondered where he could have gone.
       B I called and called his name until I was hoarse.

_____ **9. A** Just as I was about to give up, I felt a tap on my shoulder.
       B Jacob was standing behind me with an amused look on his face.

_____**10. A** I stared at him for a minute, then I stood and gave him a hug.
       B Jacob told me that he had climbed a tree behind me and found the way home.

COMPOSITION

CAUSE AND EFFECT   For each of the following words, write a
correct conjugation in the second box for the verb listed outside the box.

BASIC

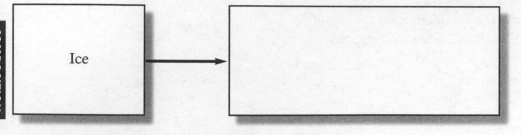

Ice ⟶ (to melt)

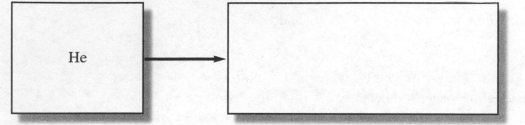

He ⟶ (to despair)

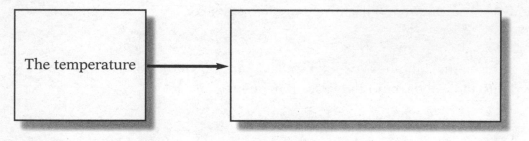

The temperature ⟶ (to despair)

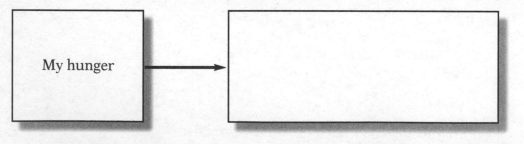

My hunger ⟶ (to grow)

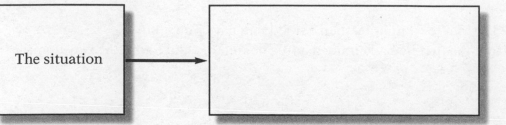

The situation ⟶ (to worsen)

DEVELOPING YOUR SKILLS
....

POINT OF VIEW   Choose whether the sentences below are written
in *first person* or *third person* point of view.

_____ **1.** The door opened and Roberto stepped into the room carrying flowers.
    A first person
    B third person

_____ **2.** She poured ice water into each glass and handed one to each of us.
    A first person
    B third person

_____ **3.** I joined the others in front of the microscope.
    A first person
    B third person

_____ **4.** When the plane stopped, we all gathered our belongings and headed for the exit.
    A first person
    B third person

_____ **5.** Nancy sat with her friends in the back of the theater.
    A first person
    B third person

_____ **6.** I told my parents I wanted to try out for the tennis team.
    A first person
    B third person

_____ **7.** Travel Club members raise money so that they can spend a weekend in
Washington D.C.
    A first person
    B third person

_____ **8.** When I was sixteen, I started taking driving lessons.
    A first person
    B third person

_____ **9.** Our parents do not let us watch TV on weekdays.
    A first person
    B third person

_____**10.** Some people think the twenty-first century starts on January 1, 2000.
    A first person
    B third person

COMPOSITION

Developing Your Skills

DESCRIPTIVE PARAGRAPHS **For each subject write a topic sentence. Tell whether your topic sentence gives a negative or a positive impression of the subject.** ADVANCED

COMPOSITION

1. a neighborhood store:

____

____

____

2. a city bus:

____

____

____

3. a fountain in the park:

____

____

____

4. a path through the forest:

____

____

____

5. a neighbor:

____

____

____

PROCESS OF WRITING A NARRATIVE PARAGRAPH

VOCABULARY

chronological order: the order in which events occur

first person narrative: the narrator participates in the story

third person narrative: the narrator does not participate in the story

descriptive writing: painting a picture with words

order of importance: the order that you relate supporting details

A Writer Writes (pages C212–C213)

Purpose: to tell a story about an imaginary discovery
Audience: newspaper readers

`BASIC/INTERMEDIATE`

Write a newspaper article about the discovery of a new continent. Be sure to tell the story of how the continent was discovered.

Purpose: to tell a story about an imaginary discovery
Audience: newspaper readers

`ADVANCED`

Write a newspaper article about the discovery of a new continent. Be sure to tell the story of how the continent was discovered. Include details about the impact of the discovery on the people living there and the plans for the use of the continent.

PROCESS OF WRITING A NARRATIVE PARAGRAPH

1. Brainstorm a list of everything you know about explorers.

2. Write a topic sentence that limits your paragraph to one major idea.

3. Use the graphic below to help you organize your narrative. Organize your ideas, then list them in the appropriate boxes.

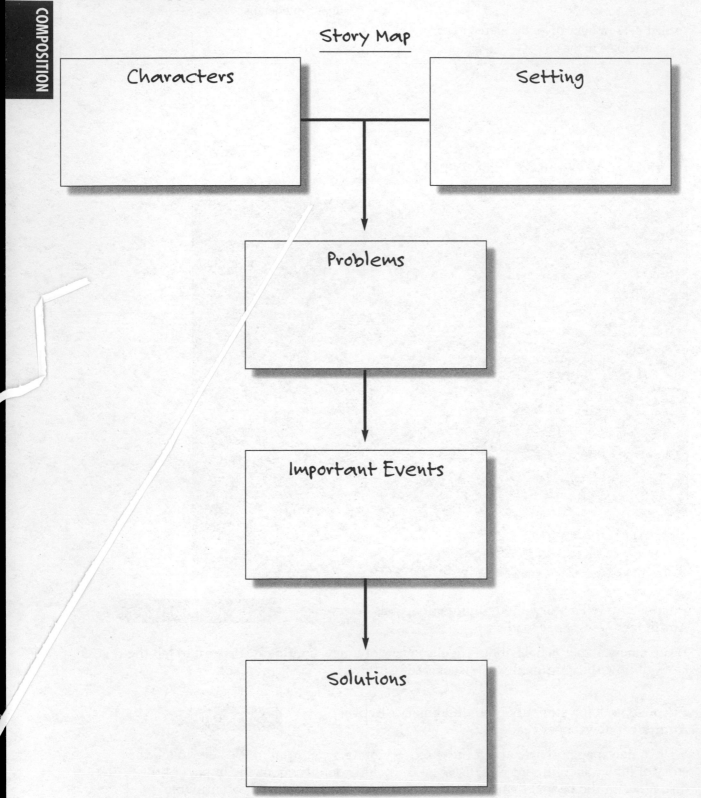

Story Map

Characters

Setting

Problems

Important Events

Solutions

GUIDED READING

Read the passage and answer the questions that follow.

FROM *When Heaven and Earth Changed Places,*
by Le Ly Hayslip

Although we grew many crops around Ky La—sweet potatoes, peanuts, cinnamon, and taro—the most important by far was rice. Yet for all its long history as the <u>staff</u> of life in our country, rice was a <u>fickle</u> provider. [**1**] First, the spot of ground on which the rice was thrown had to be just right for the seed to sprout. Then, it had to be protected from birds and animals who needed food as much as we did. As a child, I spent many hours with the other kids in Ky La acting like human scarecrow—making noise and waving our arms—just to keep the raven-like *se-se* birds away from our future supper . . .

We always blamed crop <u>failures</u> on ourselves—we had not worked hard enough or, if there was no other explanation, we had failed to <u>adequately</u> honor our ancestors. [**2**] Our solution was to pray more and sacrifice more and eventually things always got better. Crops ruined by soldiers were another matter. We knew prayer was useless because soldiers were human beings, too, and the god of nature meant for them to work out their own <u>karma</u> just like us.

In any event, the journey from seedling to rice bowl was long and <u>laborious</u> and because each grain was a symbol of life, we never wasted any of it. Good rice was considered god's gemstone—*hot ngoc troi*— and was cared for <u>accordingly</u> on pain of divine punishment. Even today a peasant seeing lightning will crouch under the table and look for lost grains in order to escape the next bolt. [**3**]

Guided Reading

1. How does the author use certain details to paint a picture?
2. What does this tell you about the narrator?
3. What is the main idea of this paragraph?

VOCABULARY

staff: stable
fickle: erratic
failures: insufficiencies
adequately: sufficiently
karma: fate
laborious: requiring hard work
accordingly: consequently

COMPOSITION

READING COMPREHENSION

____ **1.** What is the main idea of the first paragraph?
  A Rice is a fickle crop.
  B Rice was important to the author's community.
  C Brown rice is healthier than white rice.
  D The author can't stand eating rice.

____ **2.** What can you infer about the author from the second paragraph?
  A She makes excellent rice.
  B She was exposed to warfare.
  C She wishes she grew up somewhere else.
  D She loves rice.

DEVELOPING YOUR SKILLS

DETERMINING THE MEANINGS OF WORDS   For each of the following, pick *yes* if the underlined word is used correctly and *no* if it is not.

____ **1.** A simple rice dish can often taste <u>delicious</u>.
   A yes
   B no

____ **2.** I love to get up early in the <u>mourning</u>.
   A yes
   B no

____ **3.** He rode his horse out on the <u>plane</u>.
   A yes
   B no

____ **4.** The deadline was <u>extended</u>.
   A yes
   B no

____ **5.** She <u>extended</u> her arm to me.
   A yes
   B no

____ **6.** This result was not what we <u>extended</u>.
   A yes
   B no

____ **7.** She paid <u>homage</u> to her ancestors.
   A yes
   B no

____ **8.** I carried <u>there</u> suitcases.
   A yes
   B no

____ **9.** The <u>whether</u> turned cold and windy yesterday.
   A yes
   B no

____ **10.** The sun rose and <u>shown</u> its rays from high in the sky.
   A yes
   B no

DEVELOPING YOUR SKILLS

ADDING PREFIXES   A prefix is a word that has its own meaning. It is added to the front of a word. When a prefix is added to a word, it creates a new word with a new meaning.

Add one of the prefixes below to each of the five words listed and write the new word in the appropriate star.

1. belief
2. enjoyable
3. date
4. trust
5. enchanted

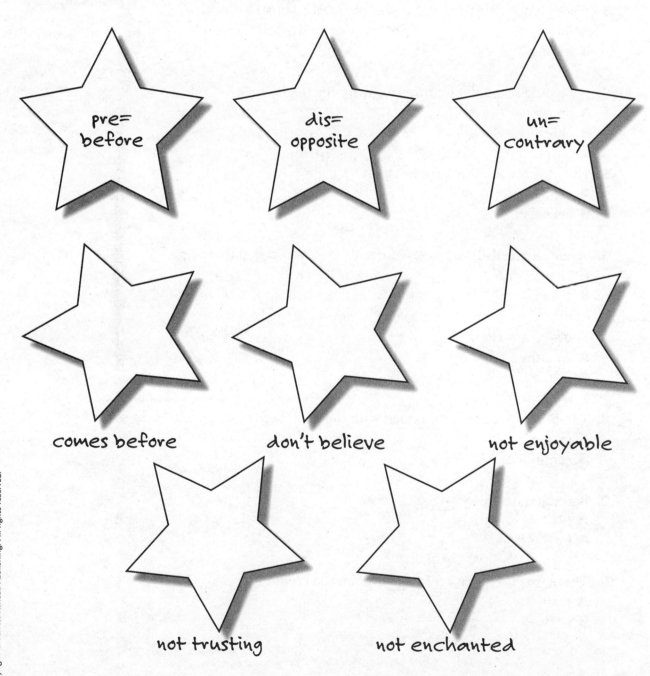

pre=
before

dis=
opposite

un=
contrary

comes before

don't believe

not enjoyable

not trusting

not enchanted

DEVELOPING YOUR SKILLS

DETERMINING WORD MEANINGS   **For each of the following**
pick the meaning of the underlined word.

_____ **1.** The separation of stalk and rice was done in a special area.
    A taking apart
    B putting away

_____ **2.** In August, when the ground was wet, we cut the plant halfway up.
    A part of the way
    B midway

_____ **3.** Transplanting the rice stalks was primarily women's work.
    A mostly
    B hardly

_____ **4.** We would bring the mature rice from the fields.
    A grown
    B elderly

_____ **5.** The grains were out of their shells.
    A remnants
    B kernels

_____ **6.** When the seeds had grown into stalks we would pull them up.
    A stems
    B stingers

_____ **7.** The soil was rich.
    A wealthy
    B fertile

_____ **8.** The broken rice that remained with the good kernels was called tam rice.
    A stayed
    B reminded

_____ **9.** Parents must never strike children.
    A hit
    B boycott

_____ **10.** There was no other way to transplant the seedlings.
    A translate
    B move

DEVELOPING YOUR SKILLS

DETERMINING THE MEANINGS OF WORDS **The following words have more than one meaning. Write a sentence for each of the meanings indicated.**

1. lead (material)

_____

lead (past tense of 'to lead')

_____

2. work (job)

_____

work (effort)

_____

3. stall (stand at a market)

_____

stall (unable to start)

_____

4. cover (of a book)

_____

cover (to conceal)

_____

5. act (to do something)

_____

act (law)

_____

PROCESS OF WRITING A COMPOSITION ABOUT CULTURAL IDENTITY

VOCABULARY

composition: an idea developed in three or more paragraphs

thesis statement: the stated main idea of a composition

tone: the writer's attitude

supporting paragraphs: paragraphs that develop the thesis statement

A Writer Writes (pages C245–C246)

Rich textiles are an inherent part of Guatemalan tradition.

Purpose: to inform others about an aspect of your own culture

Audience: your classmates and teacher

BASIC/INTERMEDIATE

In the passage by Le Ly Hayslip, she describes the significance of rice in Vietnamese culture. Think about something that is important in your own culture. Write a paragraph about it for your class.

Purpose: to inform others about an aspect of your own culture

Audience: your classmates and teacher

ADVANCED

In the passage by Le Ly Hayslip, she describes the significance of rice in Vietnamese culture. Think about something that is important in your own culture. Write a paragraph explaining the significance of this item in your culture and why it is important.

PROCESS OF WRITING A COMPOSITION ABOUT CULTURAL IDENTITY

1. Freewrite for five minutes about things that are important in your culture.
2. Pick one idea from your freewriting that you think is the most interesting.
3. Use the graphic below to help you organize your ideas.

▷ **GUIDED READING**

Read the passage and answer the questions that follow.

FROM *Barrio Boy*, by Ernesto Galarza

We could not have moved to a neighborhood less like the *barrio*. All the families around us were Americans. [1] The grumpy retired farmer next door viewed us with alarm and never gave us the time of day, but the Harrisons across the street were cordial. [2] Mr. Harrison loaned us his tools, and Roy, just my age but twice my weight, teamed up with me at once for an exchange of visits to his mother's kitchen and ours. I astounded him with my Mexican rice, and Mrs. Harrison baked my first waffle. [3] Roy and I also found a common bond in the matter of sisters. He had an older one and by now I had two younger ones. It was a question between us whether they were worse a little nuisances or as big bosses. The answer didn't make much difference but it was a relief to have another man to talk with. . . .

Since Roy had a bicycle and could get away from his sister by pedaling off on long journeys, I persuaded my family to match my savings for a used one. Together we pushed beyond the boundaries of Oak Park miles out, nearly to Perkins and the Slough House. . . . With a bike I was able to sign on as a carrier of the *Sacramento Bee*, learning in due course the art of slapping folded newspapers against people's porches instead of into the bushes or on their roofs. . . .

For the three men of the household as well as for me the bicycle became the most important means for earning a living.

Guided Reading

1. What makes the new neighborhood unlike the *barrio*?

2. Why do you think the farmer feels this way?

3. What does this detail show?

VOCABULARY

grumpy: irritable
cordial: polite
exchange: trade
astounded: amazed surprise
nuisances: annoyances
persuaded: convinced
boundaries: limits
course: passage of time

READING COMPREHENSION

_____ **1.** Which detail supports the idea that the two boys shared something alike?
   A Roy had a bicycle.
   B I astounded him with my Mexican rice.
   C Roy and I also found a common bond in the matter of sisters.
   D Mrs. Harrison baked my first waffle.

_____ **2.** What is the author's point of view about his new neighborhood?
   A It is not as good as his old neighborhood.
   B It is nothing like the *barrio* where he came from.
   C It is a really exciting neighborhood.
   D It is a terrible neighborhood.

DEVELOPING YOUR SKILLS

DESCRIPTIVE, SENSORY AND BACKGROUND DETAILS   Descriptive

details describe a place. Sensory details describe sights, smells, sounds and textures. Background details give information about the context of the story or character. For each of the following, choose what type of detail is given.

____ **1.** The aroma of the Mexican rice caressed my taste buds.
   A descriptive
   B sensory
   C background

____ **2.** The building was old and decrepit.
   A descriptive
   B sensory
   C background

____ **3.** Sally ran her fingers through the dog's silky fur.
   A descriptive
   B sensory
   C background

____ **4.** Ernesto was good at school.
   A descriptive
   B sensory
   C background

____ **5.** The metal door was cold and steely to her touch.
   A descriptive
   B sensory
   C background

____ **6.** Mrs. Dodson was always kind and helpful.
   A descriptive
   B sensory
   C background

____ **7.** The house stood silent and welcoming.
   A descriptive
   B sensory
   C background

____ **8.** Gustavo loved books.
   A descriptive
   B sensory
   C background

____ **9.** Mrs. Harrison's waffles were sweet and sticky.
   A descriptive
   B sensory
   C background

____**10.** José towered over six feet tall.
   A descriptive
   B sensory
   C background

COMPOSITION

FINDING DETAILS   Use a graphic like the one below to help you find descriptive, sensory, and background details for the following subjects. Complete the exercise on separate sheets of paper.

BASIC

1. My bedroom
2. My parents
3. My favorite teacher
4. My best friend
5. My best memory

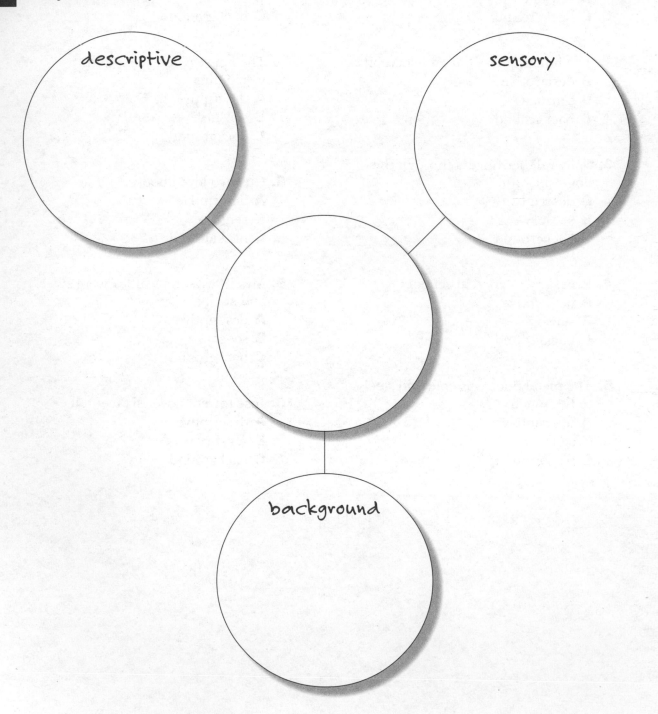

PROCESS OF WRITING A COMPOSITION ABOUT CULTURAL IDENTITY

1. Freewrite for five minutes about things that are important in your culture.

2. Pick one idea from your freewriting that you think is the most interesting.

3. Use the graphic below to help you organize your ideas.

WRITING EFFECTIVE COMPOSITIONS

▶ GUIDED READING

Read the passage and answer the questions that follow.

FROM *Barrio Boy*, by Ernesto Galarza

We could not have moved to a neighborhood less like the *barrio*. All the families around us were Americans. **[1]** The grumpy retired farmer next door viewed us with alarm and never gave us the time of day, but the Harrisons across the street were cordial. **[2]** Mr. Harrison loaned us his tools, and Roy, just my age but twice my weight, teamed up with me at once for an exchange of visits to his mother's kitchen and ours. I astounded him with my Mexican rice, and Mrs. Harrison baked my first waffle. **[3]** Roy and I also found a common bond in the matter of sisters. He had an older one and by now I had two younger ones. It was a question between us whether they were worse a little nuisances or as big bosses. The answer didn't make much difference but it was a relief to have another man to talk with. . . .

Since Roy had a bicycle and could get away from his sister by pedaling off on long journeys, I persuaded my family to match my savings for a used one. Together we pushed beyond the boundaries of Oak Park miles out, nearly to Perkins and the Slough House. . . . With a bike I was able to sign on as a carrier of the *Sacramento Bee*, learning in due course the art of slapping folded newspapers against people's porches instead of into the bushes or on their roofs. . . .

For the three men of the household as well as for me the bicycle became the most important means for earning a living.

Guided Reading

1. What makes the new neighborhood unlike the *barrio*?

2. Why do you think the farmer feels this way?

3. What does this detail show?

VOCABULARY

grumpy: irritable
cordial: polite
exchange: trade
astounded: amazed surprise
nuisances: annoyances
persuaded: convinced
boundaries: limits
course: passage of time

READING COMPREHENSION

_____ **1.** Which detail supports the idea that the two boys shared something alike?
   A Roy had a bicycle.
   B I astounded him with my Mexican rice.
   C Roy and I also found a common bond in the matter of sisters.
   D Mrs. Harrison baked my first waffle.

_____ **2.** What is the author's point of view about his new neighborhood?
   A It is not as good as his old neighborhood.
   B It is nothing like the *barrio* where he came from.
   C It is a really exciting neighborhood.
   D It is a terrible neighborhood.

DEVELOPING YOUR SKILLS

DESCRIPTIVE, SENSORY AND BACKGROUND DETAILS   Descriptive
details describe a place. Sensory details describe sights, smells, sounds and
textures. Background details give information about the context of the story
or character. For each of the following, choose what type of detail is given.

____ **1.** The aroma of the Mexican rice caressed my taste buds.
   A descriptive
   B sensory
   C background

____ **2.** The building was old and decrepit.
   A descriptive
   B sensory
   C background

____ **3.** Sally ran her fingers through the dog's silky fur.
   A descriptive
   B sensory
   C background

____ **4.** Ernesto was good at school.
   A descriptive
   B sensory
   C background

____ **5.** The metal door was cold and steely to her touch.
   A descriptive
   B sensory
   C background

____ **6.** Mrs. Dodson was always kind and helpful.
   A descriptive
   B sensory
   C background

____ **7.** The house stood silent and welcoming.
   A descriptive
   B sensory
   C background

____ **8.** Gustavo loved books.
   A descriptive
   B sensory
   C background

____ **9.** Mrs. Harrison's waffles were sweet and sticky.
   A descriptive
   B sensory
   C background

____ **10.** José towered over six feet tall.
   A descriptive
   B sensory
   C background

COMPOSITION

FINDING DETAILS   Use a graphic like the one below to help you find descriptive, sensory, and background details for the following subjects. Complete the exercise on separate sheets of paper.

COMPOSITION

1. My bedroom

2. My parents

3. My favorite teacher

4. My best friend

5. My best memory

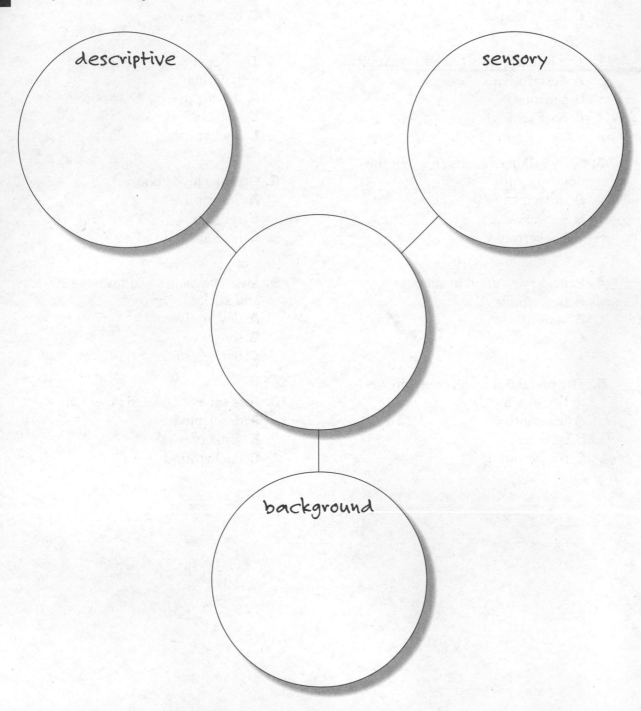

DEVELOPING YOUR SKILLS

CREATING VIVID IMAGES   Good details paint a vivid picture. For
each of the following, pick the sentence that paints the most vivid picture.

____ **1. A** The telephone looked sad from disuse.
      B The telephone did not ring.

____ **2. A** The rice was delicious.
      B The rice danced delectably on my palate.

____ **3. A** Yesterday I was so blue I could barely lift my head off my shoulders.
      B Yesterday I felt sad.

____ **4. A** The bicycle was rickety.
      B The bicycle was old.

____ **5. A** The new neighborhood was different than the *barrio*.
      B The new neighborhood could not have been less like the *barrio*.

____ **6. A** I persuaded my family to match my savings for a used bike.
      B I asked my family to match my savings for a used bike.

____ **7. A** "Call somebody," my mother urged.
      B "Call somebody," my mother said.

____ **8. A** I licked the sweet syrup off of the plate.
      B I eagerly licked the luscious syrup off the plate.

____ **9. A** The building sagged with disuse.
      B The building had not been used for a while.

____ **10. A** The boy cried in anger.
       B The boy wept with chagrin.

WRITING VIVID DETAILS   Use the following words to write a vivid
detail about the given item.

COMPOSITION

1. **item:** diamond
   words: glittered, icy

   _____

   _____

2. **item:** baseball mitt
   words: friendly, worn

   _____

   _____

3. **item:** puppy
   words: bounded, fervently

   _____

   _____

4. **item:** rat
   words: scurried, hastily

   _____

   _____

5. **item:** rainbow
   words: gleamed, beamed

   _____

   _____

PROCESS OF WRITING A COMPOSITION ABOUT CULTURAL IDENTITY

VOCABULARY

descriptive details: details that describe a place

sensory details : details that describe sights, smells, sounds and textures

background details: details that provide context

appositive phrase: group of descriptive words with no subject or verb

A Writer Writes (pages C280–C281)

Purpose: to express thoughts and feelings about a family relationship or friendship
Audience: your classmates and teacher

BASIC/INTERMEDIATE

Think of a person who is important to you. Make a list of the reasons why your relationship with this person is meaningful. Now write a paragraph explaining your feelings about this person to your class.

Purpose: to express thoughts and feelings about a family relationship or friendship
Audience: your classmates and teacher

ADVANCED

Think of a person who is important to you. Make a list of the reasons why your relationship with this person is meaningful. Now write a paragraph explaining your relationship with this person and why it is important to you. Be sure to give examples that support your feelings.

1. Make a list of every detail that makes this person important to you.

2. Using your list, pick the one detail that best expresses your feelings about this person.

3. Use the graphic below to help you organize your ideas.

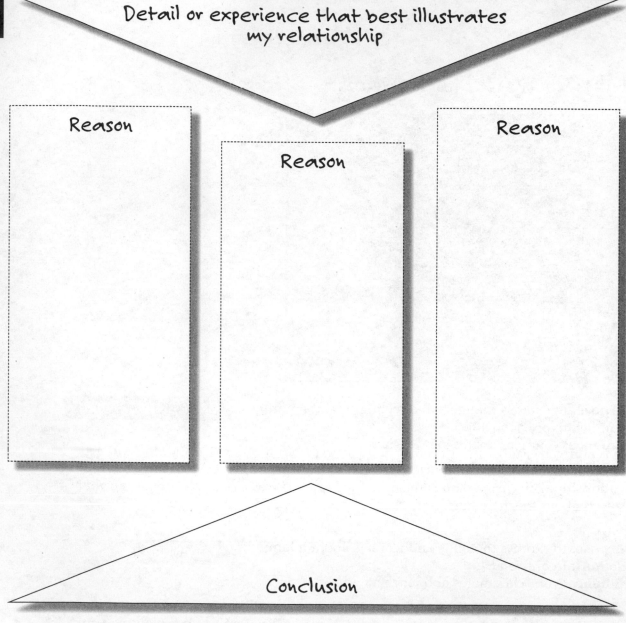

COMPOSITION

▶ GUIDED READING

Read the passage and answer the questions that follow.

FROM *Living Like Weasels*, by Annie Dillard [1]

A weasel is wild. Who knows what he thinks? He sleeps in his underground <u>den</u>, his tail draped over his nose. Sometimes he lives in his den for two days without leaving. Outside, he stalks rabbits, mice, muskrats, and birds, killing more bodies than he can eat warm, and often dragging the <u>carcasses</u> home. <u>Obedient</u> to instinct, he bites his prey at the neck, either splitting the jugular vein at the throat or crunching the brain at the base of the skull, and he does not let go. [2] One naturalist refused to kill a weasel. . . . The man could in no way pry the tiny weasel off, and he had to walk half a mile to water . . . and soak him off like a stubborn label. . . . [3]

I have been reading about weasels because I saw one last week. I <u>startled</u> a weasel who startled me, and we exchanged a long glance. . . .

Weasel! I'd never seen one wild before. He was ten inches long, thin as a curve, a muscled ribbon, brown as <u>fruitwood</u>, soft-furred, alert. His face was <u>fierce</u>, small and pointed as a lizard's; he would have made a good arrowhead. There was just a dot of chin, maybe two brown hairs' worth, and then the pure white fur began that spread sown his underside. He had two black eyes I did not see, any more than you see a window.

The weasel was <u>stunned</u> into stillness as he was emerging from beneath an enormous shaggy wildrose bush four feet away I was stunned into stillness. . . . Our eyes locked, and someone threw away the key.

Guided Reading

1. What does the title tell you about the passage?
2. How do these details support the author's ideas about weasels?
3. Why is this story included?

VOCABULARY

den: shelter
carcasses: dead bodies
obedient: complying
startled: surprised
fruitwood: the wood of fruit trees
fierce: savage
stunned: dazed

READING COMPREHENSION

____ **1.** Which detail does NOT support the idea that weasels are wild?

   A Outside, he stalks rabbits, mice, muskrats, and birds, killing more bodies than he can eat warm, and often dragging the carcasses home.

   B Obedient to instinct, he bites his prey at the neck.

   C He sleeps in his underground den.

   D He was ten inches long.

____ **2.** Which statement expresses an opinion?

   A I'd never seen one wild before.

   B He would have made a good arrowhead.

   C Our eyes locked.

   D He had two black eyes.

DESCRIPTIVE WRITING   Descriptive writing creates a vivid picture with words. For the following sentences, choose *yes* if the sentence is a good example of descriptive writing and *no* if it is not.

BASIC

____ **1.** He was ten inches long, thin as a curve, soft-furred, alert.
  A yes
  B no

____ **2.** She put the lid on the bin.
  A yes
  B no

____ **3.** He walked down the street and turned around.
  A yes
  B no

____ **4.** Annie locked eyes with the weasel, held her breath, and froze.
  A yes
  B no

____ **5.** The weasel was stunned into stillness.
  A yes
  B no

____ **6.** I waited, motionless, my spirit pleading.
  A yes
  B no

____ **7.** He picked up the ball and gave it to her.
  A yes
  B no

____ **8.** The weasel was brown.
  A yes
  B no

____ **9.** There were tracks in the clay.
  A yes
  B no

____**10.** The curious, tiny and mysterious tracks disappeared suddenly.
  A yes
  B no

DEVELOPING YOUR SKILLS

SENSORY DIAGRAM   Use a graphic like the one below to help you find sensory details for the following, writing the general idea in the space in the center and specific details on the branching lines. Use a separate sheet of paper to complete the exercise.

1. A crowded park

2. A movie theater

3. My school at lunch time

4. My school during summertime

5. A puppy

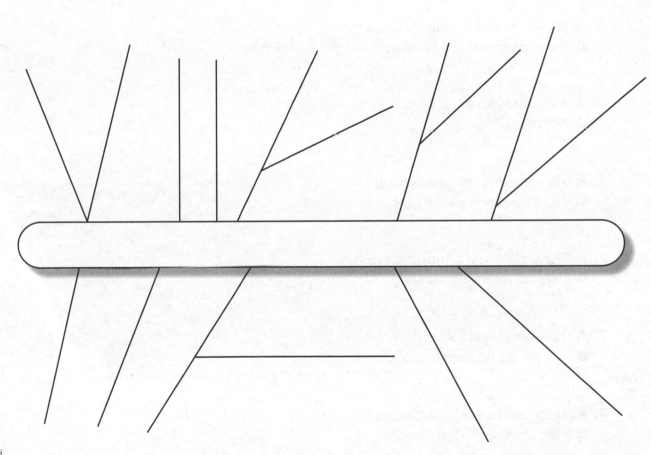

COMPOSITION

DEVELOPING YOUR SKILLS

USING FIGURATIVE LANGUAGE   Good details often paint a vivid picture using figurative language. Figurative language is a sentence or phrase compares one thing to another. For each of the following, pick the sentence that contains figurative language.

____ **1. A** Spotted hyenas are the sharks of the savanna.
     B Spotted hyenas are dangerous.

____ **2. A** I was drowning in a sea of troubles.
     B I had a lot of problems that worried me.

____ **3. A** He knocked the water bowl over.
     B He pounced on the bowl of water like it was prey.

____ **4. A** She cried like a baby
     B She cried a lot.

____ **5. A** The new moon was a beacon.
     B The new moon shone in the sky.

____ **6. A** The weasel was a muscled ribbon.
     B The weasel was muscular.

____ **7. A** The sound was soft.
     B The sound floated down, as soft as down.

____ **8. A** The wind carried a stream of odors.
     B The wind carried the smells.

____ **9. A** His expressionless face was as cold as cement.
     B He was expressionless and cold.

____**10. A** He moved quickly.
     B He moved like a deer.

DEVELOPING YOUR SKILLS

WRITING DESCRIPTIONS USING FIGURATIVE LANGUAGE

Write a sentence that uses figurative language to compare following items.

1. the ocean
a mirror

_____

_____

2. a kitten
a wool sweater

_____

_____

3. fog
cotton

_____

_____

4. a sneaker
a worn glove

_____

_____

5. a runner
a cougar

_____

_____

VOCABULARY

descriptive writing: creates a vivid picture in words

objective observation: stating facts without opinions

subjective observation: an observation colored by feelings or beliefs

A Writer Writes (pages C319–C320)

In many cases, bad conditions can be changed when people get concerned and involved.

Purpose: to record accurately and forcefully the outward signs of a problem that needs fixing   **BASIC/INTERMEDIATE**

Audience: fellow citizens and elected officials who could make a difference

Think of something that you feel is a problem. It could be global warming, the need for renewable energy source, the state of your local park or the condition of your room at home. Write a short essay describing the terrible condition of this problem.

Purpose: to record accurately and forcefully the outward signs of a problem that needs fixing   **ADVANCED**

Audience: fellow citizens and elected officials who could make a difference

Think of something that you feel is a problem. It could be something large, like global warming, or something personal, like the condition of your room at home. Write a short essay describing the awful conditions of this problem. Be sure to use specific details that will support your opinion so that others will not doubt that this is, indeed, a problem about which something must be done.

PROCESS OF WRITING A DESCRIPTION OF A PROBLEM

1. Freewrite for five minutes about the problem you have picked.
2. Pick the most compelling detail from your freewriting and use that as the basis of your essay.
3. Use the graphic below to help you organize your ideas.

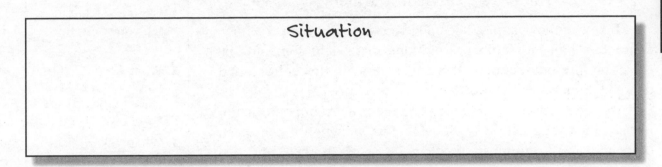

Situation

Cause or Effect	Cause or Effect	Cause or Effect

Evidence	Evidence	Evidence

Conclusion

COMPOSITION

CREATIVE WRITING: STORIES, PLAYS, AND POEMS

▶ GUIDED READING

Read the passage and answer the questions that follow.

FROM *'The Past and Its Power: Why I Wrote "The Price"'*, by Arthur Miller [1]

Like the movies, plays seemed to exist entirely in the now; characters had either no pastor none that could somehow be directing present actions. It was as though the culture had decreed amnesia as the ultimate mark of reality. [2]

As the corpses piled up, it became cruelly impolite if not unpatriotic to suggest the obvious, that we were fighting the past; our rigid anti-Communist theology, born of another time two decades earlier, made it a sin to consider Vietnamese Reds as nationalists rather than Moscow's and Beijing's yapping dogs. [3] We were fighting in a state of forgetfulness, quite as though we had not aborted a national election in Vietnam and divided the country into separate halves when it became clear that Ho Chi Minh would be the overwhelming favorite for the presidency. This was the reality on the ground, but unfortunately it had to be recalled in order to matter. And so 50,000 Americans, not to mention millions of Vietnamese, paid with their lives to support a myth and a bellicose denial.

"The Price" grew out of a need to reconfirm the power of the past, the seedbed of current reality, and the way to possibly reaffirm cause and effect in an insane world. It seemed to me that if, through the mists of denial, the bow of the ancient ship of reality could emerge, the spectacle might once again hold some beauty for an audience.

Guided Reading

1. What does the title tell you about the passage?

2. What words in this paragraph might be clues to the article's main idea?

3. What reasons does the writer give to show that the topic is an important one?

VOCABULARY

decreed: declared
ultimate: highest
theology: religion
aborted: stopped
recalled: remembered
bellicose: warlike

READING COMPREHENSION

_____ **1.** What is the main idea of the passage?
  A The past impacts actions in the present.
  B Modern theater does not like to mention the past.
  C The Vietnam war was caused by American anti-Communism.
  D The spectacle of the past holds beauty for an audience.

_____ **2.** Based on the passage, what do you think "The Price" is about?
  A The impact of the past on the present.
  B The lack of good plays on Broadway.
  C The need to support America's military actions.
  D The importance of the here and now.

DEVELOPING YOUR SKILLS

DESCRIPTIVE TOPIC SENTENCES   **Choose the more likely detail or details to go with the following settings.**

____ **1.** an afternoon in August at the beach
  A wearing a jacket and scarf
  B sweltering from the hot sun

____ **2.** a small town in the middle of the desert
  A a tumbleweed rolling across the street
  B skyscrapers reaching for the sky

____ **3.** an evening at a amusement park near the ocean
  A cool salt-air breeze
  B hot desert wind

____ **4.** a restaurant after closing time
  A workers cleaning tables
  B customers waiting in line at the counter

____ **5.** a school cafeteria at lunchtime
  A groups of friends talking excitedly
  B silence except for the sound of crickets

____ **6.** a fall morning in the woods
  A falling leaves of brilliant colors
  B empty parking lots

____ **7.** a house without electricity on a hot summer night
  A quiet, cool, cozy
  B sweaty, tense, bewildering

____ **8.** a house without heat on a cold winter night
  A quiet, cool, cozy
  B shivering, tense, ornery

____ **9.** the night before an important exam
  A anxious
  B overjoyed

____ **10.** hang gliding on a summer morning
  A thrilled
  B sad

▶ DEVELOPING YOUR SKILLS

SKETCHING CHARACTERS   **For each of the characters given below, write on the chart one trait in each column.**

1. firefighter

2. President of the United States

3. high school teacher

4. nurse

5. mountain climber

Character	Physical	Actions	Feelings

▶ DEVELOPING YOUR SKILLS

ORDERING EVENTS For each event, choose the more likely event to follow in a realistic story.

____ **1.** Ximena opened the wooden chest.
  A Her shovel struck something hard in the soil.
  B Inside the chest were a collection of old coins and jewels.

____ **2.** Miguel asked the old man about the cave.
  A The old man told Miguel the legend of the cave.
  B Miguel looked for someone in town that could tell him about the cave.

____ **3.** I rolled out of bed and looked out the window.
  A I had a dream of a silver horse running through the woods.
  B I saw our neighbor's horse grazing in our backyard.

____ **4.** The senatorial candidate concluded her rousing speech.
  A The audience roared with approval.
  B The senatorial candidate spoke of the problems she wanted to fix.

____ **5.** Maria taught her brothers to play the game she had learned in school.
  A The next day, they taught it to some of their friends.
  B That afternoon, a circus troupe had visited her class.

____ **6.** After the softball game ended, we all skipped home.
  A I was the last one to bat.
  B On the way we stopped and picked wildflowers.

____ **7.** Ricky fell asleep reading the sports section of the newspaper.
  A When he woke up, it was time to leave for school.
  B He discovered a story hew thought would be interesting.

____ **8.** Julie and Tricia walked down the path to the beach.
  A Their mother told them where they could find some nice shells.
  B In the water they discovered the most beautiful shell they had ever seen.

____ **9.** My father looked under the hood of his old Rambler.
  A "The carburetor is broken," he said.
  B "We'll have to see what the problem is," my father sighed.

____ **10.** When he checked it was eight-fifteen there in Santa Fe.
  A He called his cousin in Spain, because he knew it was only three-fifteen there.
  B He decided to wait until the next day to call his cousin in Spain.

▶ DEVELOPING YOUR SKILLS

CHOOSING CHARACTER TRAITS For each person, write one character trait that depends on your senses, one that shows an action, one that tells a thought or feeling he or she has or had, and one that compares him or her to something or someone else.

1. a relative

_____

_____

2. a friend

_____

_____

3. a neighbor

_____

_____

4. a politician

_____

_____

5. a celebrity

_____

_____

PROCESS OF WRITING A "WHY" STORY

VOCABULARY

short story: fictional account of characters and conflict

character: a person in a story

setting: the environment where the action takes place

narrator: person who tells the story

pronoun: takes the place of a noun

nominative case pronouns: pronouns used as subjects

objective case pronouns: pronouns used as objects

play: a piece of writing that is performed

dialogue: conversation between characters in a play

poem: writing that expresses powerful emotion through language

A Writer Writes (pages C377–C378)

Purpose: to entertain
Audience: your classmates

BASIC/INTERMEDIATE

Write a fable or folktale explaining why something is the way it is. For example, a story explaining how the moon got into the sky or why trees grow moss. Think of details and characters that will make your story entertaining.

Purpose: to entertain
Audience: your classmates

ADVANCED

Write a fable or folktale for your classmates explaining how something came to be the way it is. For example, a story explaining how and why the moon came to be in the sky or a story explaining why trees grow moss. The story should be fanciful rather than literal. Use details and characters that will make your story entertaining.

PROCESS OF WRITING A "WHY" STORY
....

1. Brainstorm a list of reasons why your subject came to exist.

2. Choose the top three most compelling reasons for your folktale.

3. Use the graphic below to help you organize your ideas.

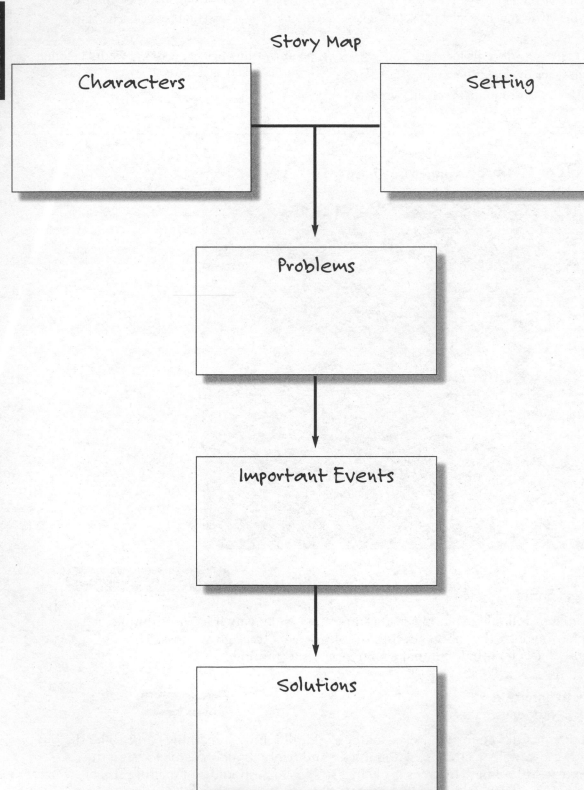

Story Map

Characters

Setting

Problems

Important Events

Solutions

GUIDED READING

Read the passage and answer the questions that follow.

FROM *Mercury, Gemini and Saturn* by Joy Hakim

Nearby, three men sat strapped elbow to elbow inside a narrow <u>capsule</u> on top of a rocket that stood as tall as a 30-story building. Neil Armstrong, a civilian pilot, was in the left seat. . . . Armstrong had the personality of a cowboy-movie hero: cool. Edwin E. Aldrin sat in the middle. Everyone called him by his school nickname, Buzz. Buzz Aldrin was an air force colonel with a big brain. Some of his scientific ideas had gone into this <u>mission</u>. Michael Collins, another air force officer and test pilot, was to pilot the command ship, which would orbit the moon while the other two men <u>descended</u> to the lunar surface in the landing vehicle.

The rocket—named Saturn—<u>belched</u> fire and its own <u>billowing</u> clouds, lifted off, and seemed to rise slowly. [1] But that was an <u>illusion</u>; after two and a half minutes Saturn was 41 miles above Earth. [2] It was traveling at 5,400 mph (miles per hour) when its first stage fell away. (How fast can an automobile go? How about a commercial jet?)

The next stage took the astronauts 110 miles above Earth, carrying them at 14,000 mph, and was <u>jettisoned</u> . . . The third stage got them to 17,400 mph; they were now weightless and orbiting the earth. It was 17 minutes after liftoff. After they had circled the globe twice, the third-stage engine fired the ship away from Earth's orbit. [3] "It was beautiful," said Armstrong. He was <u>cruising</u> toward the moon.

Guided Reading

1. What effect do the words "belched" and "billowing" create?

2. What words help create a feeling of amazement?

3. Why do you think the author includes this information?

VOCABULARY

capsule: receptacle
mission: assignment
illusion: deception
belched: erupted
billowing: blowing
jettisoned: dropped away
cruising: travelling

READING COMPREHENSION

_____ **1.** Which detail does supports the notion that rocket technology is impressive?

   A Some of his scientific ideas had gone into this mission.

   B The third stage got them to 17,400 mph.

   C Nearby, three men sat strapped elbow to elbow inside a narrow capsule on top of a rocket.

   D Armstrong had the personality of a cowboy-movie hero: cool.

_____ **2.** Based on the details in the passage, how do you think the author feels about the moon-landing?

   A That it is an important and impressive event.

   B That it was not that interesting.

   C That people paid it too much attention.

   D That the money spent on NASA would have been better-spent elsewhere.

▶ DEVELOPING YOUR SKILLS

STEPS IN A PROCESS   In order to write an essay that informs or explains, you need to be able to organize the information that you have. This means stating the information in a way that is clear to readers. For the following sentences, pick *yes* if the information in the sentence is organized and clear, and *no* if it is not.

BASIC

____ **1.** Janice picked up the phone and dialed the number.
     A Yes
     B No

____ **2.** Claire watched the television show and turned on the TV.
     A Yes
     B No

____ **3.** The airplane took off down the runway and loaded the passengers.
     A Yes
     B No

____ **4.** Roy sat down, softly strummed his guitar, and began to sing.
     A Yes
     B No

____ **5.** The subway stop is near my house but far from the school.
     A Yes
     B No

____ **6.** The red vase was on the table two feet from the window.
     A Yes
     B No

____ **7.** He took the exam and then he studied.
     A Yes
     B No

____ **8.** She made omelets and broke some eggs.
     A Yes
     B No

____ **9.** The rocket burst into the sky and the countdown ended and the crowd gathered.
     A Yes
     B No

____ **10.** The car went 30 mph, the truck 20 mph and the train 80 mph.
     A Yes
     B No

DEVELOPING YOUR SKILLS

SENSORY DIAGRAM   Information can also be organized in order of importance, interest, size, or degree. Using the graphic, organize the following items according to the direction at the end of each list. Use a separate sheet of paper to complete the activity.

1. a large pizza, a potato chip, a slice of cake, a pea, an apple [size]

2. a senator, the President of the United States, a city mayor, a governor, your class president [importance of office]

3. the sun, a burning match, a gas stove, a forest fire, a camp fire [degree of heat]

4. a rat, a dog, an elephant, a camel, a hummingbird [size]

5. a story about a neighborhood, a story about the declaration of World Peace, a story about local politics, a story about federal government, a story about state taxes [interest to international readers]

▷ DEVELOPING YOUR SKILLS

TYPES OF ORDER   In order to write an essay that informs or
explains, you need to be able to organize the information that you have.
This requires putting the information in a sequence that readers can
understand. *Chronological order* presents information in the order in
which it occurred. *Spatial order* gives information according to location.
   For each of the following sentences, identify the type of order used.

INTERMEDIATE

____ **1.** First I called my mom and then I called my brother.
   A Chronological order
   B Spatial order

____ **2.** Mark's house is two blocks from my house, three miles from John's house and 15
   miles from school.
   A Chronological order
   B Spatial order

____ **3.** I started by beating in the eggs, then added the sugar and salt.
   A Chronological order
   B Spatial order

____ **4.** John is standing next to me, four feet from Jenny and six feet from Bill.
   A Chronological order
   B Spatial order

____ **5.** First you will see the store and then the church and gas station.
   A Chronological order
   B Spatial order

____ **6.** Look for the City Hall, it is near the Town Square and across from the tennis court.
   A Chronological order
   B Spatial order

____ **7.** Jerry woke up, stretched his arms and swung his feet to the floor.
   A Chronological order
   B Spatial order

____ **8.** Mary walked to the gym and then made her way to the ice-cream parlor.
   A Chronological order
   B Spatial order

____ **9.** The car raced past the first marker, buzzed by the second marker and sped to the
   finish line.
   A Chronological order
   B Spatial order

____**10.** The balloon floated 10 feet above the ground, 7 feet above the table and 4 feet above
   my head.
   A Chronological order
   B Spatial order

 **DEVELOPING YOUR SKILLS**

WRITING SENTENCES USING PRONOUNS **Combine each set of** three sentences below and place them in logical order. ADVANCED

1. Beth called me.

I left a message for Beth.

We made a date.

_____

_____

2. They watched the show together.

Alma called for reservations.

Pierre suggested they see the show.

_____

_____

3. The rocket was 175 miles above the earth.

The kite was 30 feet above the earth.

The plane was 20,000 feet above the earth.

_____

_____

4. Laila tried again.

Philippe exclaimed, "No, no, no!"

Laila tried to complete the exercise.

_____

_____

5. Sally put out the fresh food.

The cat ran towards the bowl.

Sally called "here kitty, kitty."

_____

_____

COMPOSITION

PROCESS OF WRITING A SCIENCE ARTICLE

COMPOSITION

A Writer Writes (pages C427–C428)

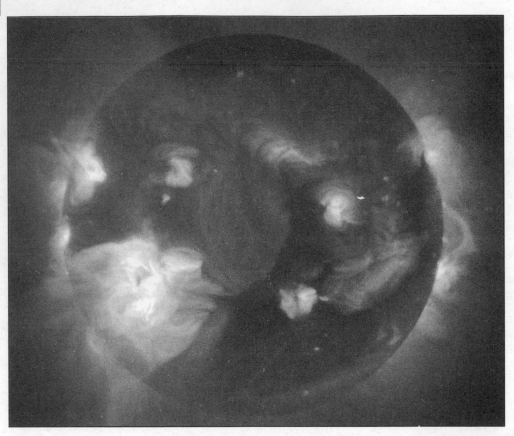

Purpose: to explain an aspect of outer space that would interest and enlighten children
Audience: students in the fourth or fifth grade

BASIC/INTERMEDIATE

Think of something interesting about space travel. Then, use the Internet or a magazine to look up information about the thing you picked. Write a short essay suitable for fourth grade students explaining your topic.

Purpose: to explain an aspect of outer space that would interest and enlighten children
Audience: students in the fourth or fifth grade

ADVANCED

Think of something interesting about space travel. Then, use the Internet or a magazine to look up specific information about the thing you picked. Write a short essay suitable for fourth grade students explaining your topic and why it is interesting. Be sure to include details that support your opinion.

PROCESS OF WRITING A SCIENCE ARTICLE

1. Brainstorm a list of reasons why you find your topic interesting.

2. Choose the top three most interesting reasons from your brainstorming.

3. Use the graphic below to help you organize your ideas.

Situation		
Cause or Effect	Cause or Effect	Cause or Effect
Evidence	Evidence	Evidence
Conclusion		

GUIDED READING

Read the passage and answer the questions that follow.

FROM *Are Native American Team Nicknames Offensive?*,
by Gary Kimble and Bob DiBiasio [1]

Any kind of portrayal of Native Americans that isn't respectful bothers me. Too many times, we're portrayed as hostile and criminal, as some kind of blood-thirsty savages. Or we're noble savages, nobler than other people because supposedly we're closer to nature. Both portrayals are stereotypes. Anytime you turn people into symbols and move away from reality, that's bad. [2]

A lot of people are offended by caricatures such as the one the Cleveland Indians use for their logo. When you do a caricature, you're dealing with someone's identity, and that puts you on thin ice. Even the name makes you wonder. They wouldn't call themselves the "Cleveland White People" or the "Cleveland Black People."

—Gary N. Kimble, commissioner for the Administration
for Native Americans in the Department of Health
and Human Services, Washington, D.C.

Any discussion of the Cleveland Indians' name and the team logo, Chief Wahoo, must begin with a history lesson. Not many people realize the origin of "Indians," but there is a historical significance to how the Cleveland franchise got its name.

. . . Indians was selected in honor of Louis Francis Sockalexis, a Penobscot Indian who was the first Native American to play professional baseball. [3]

Newspaper accounts at the time reported that the name Indians was chosen as "a testament to the game's first American Indian." Today, 79 years later, we're proud to acknowledge and foster the legacy of Scokalexis.

—Bob DiBiasio, Vice-President of Public
Relations for the Cleveland Indians

Guided Reading

1. What clues does the title give you about the articles?

2. What words in this paragraph might be clues to the article's main idea?

3. What reasons does the author give to support his idea that there is a historical significance to how the Cleveland team got its name?

VOCABULARY

portrayal: depiction
stereotypes: oversimplified conceptions
offended: insulted
caricatures: grotesque impersonation
testament: evidence

READING COMPREHENSION

____ 1. What is the main idea of the articles?
   A To show that "Indians" is an offensive name.
   B To show that "Indians" is not an offensive name.
   C To persuade readers to boycott baseball.
   D To show the pros and cons of Native American sports team nicknames.

____ 2. Based on the details in the first passage, what do you think is the author's point of view regarding the Cleveland Indians?
   A He thinks that it is offensive to Native Americans.
   B He thinks that it honors Native Americans.
   C He thinks it is "cool."
   D He does not have an opinion, one way or the other.

DEVELOPING YOUR SKILLS

IDENTIFYING YOUR AUDIENCE   In order to write an effective persuasive essay, you need to know who your audience is. For each of the following sentences, pick the audience for whom you think the sentence is intended.

BASIC

_____ **1.** Students should not have to work so hard in school.
A students
B parents

_____ **2.** MTV helps promote good study skills.
A students
B parents

_____ **3.** Students who study for 4 hours a night do better in college.
A students
B parents

_____ **4.** Speech and debate make students better leaders.
A students
B parents

_____ **5.** Jazz Jeans look cool.
A students
B parents

_____ **6.** Jazz Jeans last longer than other jeans.
A students
B parents

_____ **7.** Dixon School is a good investment in the future.
A students
B parents

_____ **8.** Dixon School builds lifetime friendships.
A students
B parents

_____ **9.** Dixon School is fun and laid-back.
A students
B parents

_____ **10.** Dixon School will make you popular.
A students
B parents

COMPOSITION

▶ DEVELOPING YOUR SKILLS

PROS AND CONS   Imagine that you are going to argue the following proposals. Use the graphic organizer below to list the pros and the cons of each.

1. A new theater in your school
2. Free notebooks for all students
3. A new sports facility at your school
4. Shorter school days
5. More holidays during school

Idea	Pros	Cons
1.		
2.		
3.		
4.		
5.		

▶ DEVELOPING YOUR SKILLS

IDENTIFYING YOUR AUDIENCE   Imagine that you wanted to start a theater for kids on your block. Decide whether the following statements would be more persuasive to the *kids* in your neighborhood or to the *parents*. If you think both groups would find them persuasive, choose *both*.

____ **1.** A theatre would be a great way for all the kids to get to know each other.
   A kids
   B parents
   C both

____ **2.** A parent has volunteered to supervise the theatre's productions.
   A kids
   B parents
   C both

____ **3.** The kids could perform write and perform anything they wanted.
   A kids
   B parents
   C both

____ **4.** Theatre is cool and performing is a thrill.
   A kids
   B parents
   C both

____ **5.** The experience working on plays could help kids succeed in school.
   A kids
   B parents
   C both

____ **6.** Writing, performing and directing plays is creative and fun.
   A kids
   B parents
   C both

____ **7.** Kids could charge money for the performances.
   A kids
   B parents
   C both

____ **8.** One family has already donated space to use as a theatre.
   A kids
   B parents
   C both

____ **9.** The cost of doing the plays would be low because kids would make all of their costumes.
   A kids
   B parents
   C both

____ **10.** Performing for the neighborhood would be really fun.
   A kids
   B parents
   C both

▷ DEVELOPING YOUR SKILLS

PERSUASIVE TOPIC SENTENCES   **Write a persuasive topic sentence**   `ADVANCED`
for each of the following topics.

COMPOSITION

1. T.V. has too many commercials.

_____

_____

2. People should use mass transportation.

_____

_____

3. People should fight to save the rainforests.

_____

_____

4. People should read the newspaper.

_____

_____

5. Pro-athletes should be considered heroes.

_____

_____

PROCESS OF WRITING A PERSUASIVE ESSAY

VOCABULARY

persuasive essay: an essay written to convince readers

fact: a statement that can be proved

opinion: a belief or judgment that cannot be proved

introduction: captures reader's attention

body of supporting paragraphs: presents reasons, facts and examples

conclusion: drives home writer's opinions

A Writer Writes (pages C465–C466)

Purpose: to persuade adults in authority to regulate video games in some way or to oppose regulation
Audience: law makers or video game producers

BASIC/INTERMEDIATE

Some people argue that video games are too realistic and violent and that they may promote violence in the teenagers who play them. Others argue that video games are a harmless way for kids to "blow off steam." Decide which side of the argument you agree with and write a persuasive essay. Be sure to say why you feel the way you do.

Purpose: to persuade adults in authority to regulate video games in some way or to oppose regulation
Audience: law makers or video game producers

ADVANCED

Some people argue that video games are too realistic and violent and that they may promote violence in the teenagers who play them. Others argue that video games are a harmless way for kids to "blow off steam." Decide which side of the argument you agree with and write a persuasive essay presenting your opinion. Be sure to give reasons that support why you feel the way you do and why others should feel the same way.

PROCESS OF WRITING A PERSUASIVE ESSAY

1. Freewrite for five minutes about your opinion and why you feel the way you do.
2. Make a list of the most compelling reasons in your freewriting.
3. Use the graphic below to help you organize your ideas.

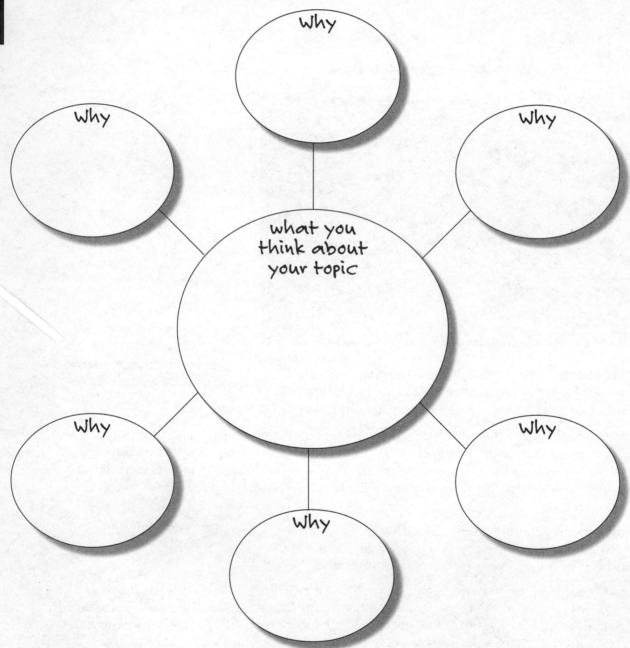

COMPOSITION

▶ GUIDED READING

Read the passage and answer the questions that follow.

FROM *Say It With Flowers*, by Toshio Mori [1]

"When the customers ask you <u>whether</u> the flowers are fresh, say yes firmly. 'Our flowers are always fresh, madam.'"

Teruo picked up a vase of carnations. "These flowers came in four or five days ago, didn't they?" he asked me.

"You're right. Five days ago," I said.

"How long will they <u>keep</u> if a customer bought them today?" Teruo asked.

"I guess in this weather they'll <u>hold</u> a day or two," I said.

"Then they're old," Teruo almost <u>gasped</u>. [2] "Why, we have fresh ones that last a week or so in the shop."

"Sure, Teruo. And why should you worry about that?" Tommy said. "You talk right to the customers and they'll believe you. 'Our flowers are always fresh? You bet they are! Just came in a little while ago form the market.'"

Teruo looked at us calmly, "That's a hard thing to say when you know it isn't true."

"You've got to get it over with sooner or later," I told him. "Everybody has to do it. You too, unless you want to lose your job."

"I don't think I can say it <u>convincingly</u> again," Teruo said. "I must have said yes forty times already when I didn't know any better. It'll be harder next time." [3]

Guided Reading

1. What can you determine about the author's attitude by the title?

2. What effect does the word *gasped* have?

3. Why do you think Teruo says this?

VOCABULARY

whether: if

keep: last

hold: last

gasped: breathed in sharply

convincingly: persuasively

READING COMPREHENSION

____ 1. Which detail supports the idea that Teruo does not like the idea of being dishonest?

    A "I guess in this weather they'll hold a day or two"

    B "I don't think I can say it convincingly again"

    C "How do you tell when a flower is fresh or old?"

    D "Sure, Teruo. And why should you worry about that?"

____ 2. Based on the story, what do you think is the author's point of view regarding the narrator?

    A He is a good worker.

    B He is more honest than Teruo.

    C He is not as honest as Teruo.

    D He has a lot to learn about selling flowers.

GATHERING EVIDENCE   In order to prove your thesis in a critical essay you must supply evidence for your reader.   **BASIC**

For each of the following sentences, pick *yes* if you think the sentence supports the thesis statement that "dogs make good pets" and *no* if it does not.

_____ **1.** Dogs are loyal and loving.
    A yes
    B no

_____ **2.** Dogs can be trained to do useful things, such as bring in the newspaper.
    A yes
    B no

_____ **3.** Dogs sometimes bite people.
    A yes
    B no

_____ **4.** Some dogs have too much fur.
    A yes
    B no

_____ **5.** My neighbor's dog barks nonstop.
    A yes
    B no

_____ **6.** My dog saved my life.
    A yes
    B no

_____ **7.** Surveys show that people who have dogs are happier than people who do not.
    A yes
    B no

_____ **8.** Dogs are always happy to see you.
    A yes
    B no

_____ **9.** Dogs can guard your home and keep you safe.
    A yes
    B no

_____ **10.** It is fun to take dogs for a walk.
    A yes
    B no

GATHERING EVIDENCE—WORD WEB   Imagine that you are going to write a paragraph about *Say It With Flowers*. Use the word web to organize the statements listed below. Use a separate sheet of paper to complete the exercise, creating a separate word web for each statement.

1. Teruo is eager to learn the flower business

2. Teruo is honest.

3. Tommy and the narrator do not tell the truth.

4. The narrator and Tommy want to keep their jobs.

5. Teruo does not think he can lie.

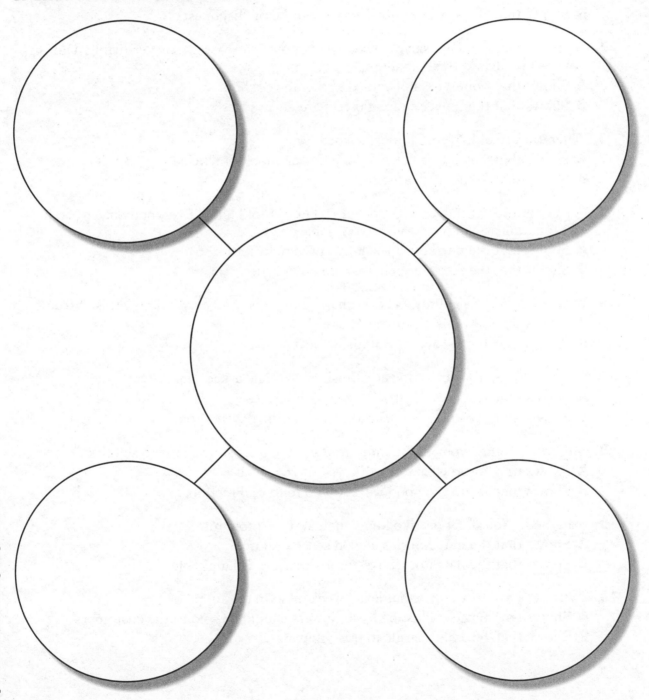

GATHERING EVIDENCE   When writing critical essays, it is important to find evidence that supports your ideas in the passage. For each of the following quotes from the story, pick the idea it better supports.

_____ **1.** "It'll be harder next time."
   A Shows that Teruo does not want to lie.
   B Shows that Teruo cannot follow directions.

_____ **2.** "Sure, Teruo. And why should you worry about that?" Tommy said.
   A Shows that Tommy does not like Teruo.
   B Shows that Tommy does not worry about being dishonest.

_____ **3.** "When the customers ask you whether the flowers are fresh, say yes firmly. 'Our flowers are always fresh, madam.'"
   A Shows that honesty is not valued at the flower shop.
   B Shows that the flower shop's flowers are always fresh.

_____ **4.** "Then they're old," Teruo almost gasped.
   A Shows that Teruo is shocked by the flower shop's practices.
   B Shows that Teruo is pleased.

_____ **5.** "You've got to get it over with sooner or later," I told him. "Everybody has to do it. You too, unless you want to lose your job."
   A Shows that the narrator does not want to help Teruo.
   B Shows that the narrator believes that lying is necessary.

_____ **6.** Teruo looked at us calmly, "That's a hard thing to say when you know it isn't true."
   A Shows that Teruo is a calm character.
   B Shows that Teruo cares about his integrity.

_____ **7.** "How do you tell when a flower is fresh or old?" he asked me.
   A Shows that Teruo wants to do a good job.
   B Shows that Teruo has not learned much at the flower shop.

_____ **8.** "All I do is follow your instructions and sell the ones you tell me to sell first."
   A Shows that Teruo is lazy at work.
   B Shows that Teruo is a good worker who follows directions.

_____ **9.** I laughed. "You don't need to know that, Teruo," I told him.
   A Shows that the narrator has a good sense of humor.
   B Shows that the narrator thinks Teruo's concern is laughable.

_____ **10.** "Why, we have fresh ones that last a week or so in the shop."
   A Shows that Teruo thinks the fresh flowers should be sold to the customers.
   B Shows that Teruo is allergic to fresh flowers.

DEVELOPING YOUR SKILLS
. . . .

GATHERING EVIDENCE   For each of the following quotes, write down
what idea you think it supports.

1. When I went out to the truck to make my last delivery for the day Teruo followed me. "Gee I feel rotten," he said to me. "Those flowers I sold to the people, the won't last longer than tomorrow."

   _____

   _____

2. Then one early morning, the inevitable happened. While Teruo was selling the fresh flowers in the back to a customer, Mr. Sasaki came in quietly and watched the transaction. . . . All day Teruo looked sick.

   _____

   _____

3. "You fellows teach me something about this business and I'll be grateful. I want to start from the bottom," Teruo said.

   _____

   _____

4. "How long will they keep if a customer bought them today?" Teruo asked.

   _____

   _____

5. "Do we like it? Do you think we're any different from you?" Tommy asked Teruo. "You're just a green kid. You don't know any better so I don't get sore, but you got to play the game when you're in it."

   _____

   _____

COMPOSITION

VOCABULARY

literary analysis: an interpretation of literature

climax: high-point of a story

motivation: why a character does something

alliteration: using words together that start with the same letter or sound

onomatopoeia: word that sound like what they are or do

simile: a comparison using "like" or "as"

metaphor: a comparison where one thing is used to describe another

A Writer Writes (pages C514–C515)

Many poets are inspired by nature and natural wonders.

Purpose: to explain your response to a poem
Audience: peer readers

BASIC/INTERMEDIATE

Pick a poem that you like and write a literary analysis of it. Be sure to include what you think the poem is saying and why you think it is effective.

Purpose: to explain your response to a poem
Audience: peer readers

ADVANCED

Pick a poem that you like and write a literary analysis of it. Be sure to include what you think the poem is saying and why you think it is effective. Consider factors such as rhythm, rhyme scheme, alliteration and figures of speech when discussing the poem.

PROCESS OF WRITING A LITERARY ANALYSIS OF A POEM

1. Make a list of the things you like about the poem.

2. Put your list into categories, such as "figurative language" or "main idea."

3. Use the word web below to help you organize your ideas.

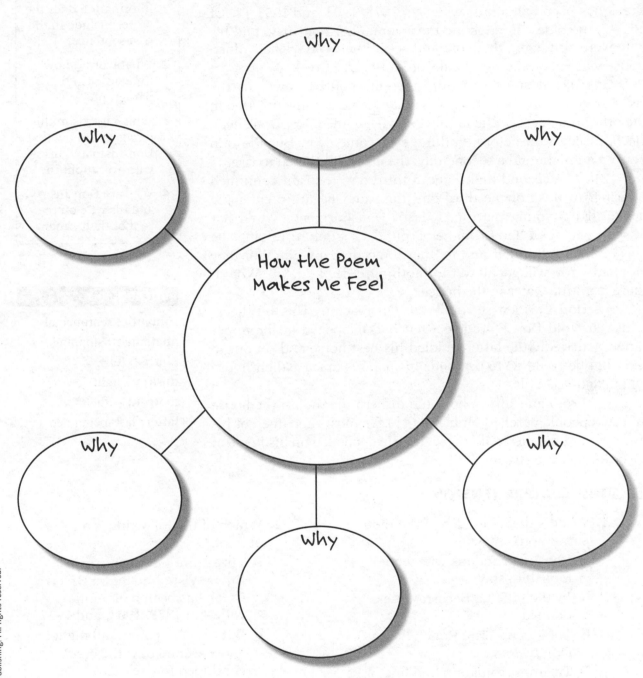

COMPOSITION

▶ GUIDED READING

....

Read the passage and answer the questions that follow.

FROM *Rancho Buena Vista,* by Fermina Guerra

Three times in the history of Buena Vista Ranch, La Becerra Creek has been half a mile wide—in 1878, 1903, and 1937. **[1]** Of course, the oldest flood is the most <u>romantic</u>. Don Justo and his wife were still living then, old and set in their ways. Their ranch house was . . . on the very banks of La Becerra Creek.

One day it started to rain; torrents poured down. As the creek began to rise and there was no <u>abatement</u> of the downpour, the other members of the family grew frightened. Not Don Justo. [. . .] seen rain before; nothing ever came of it. But the rain [. . .]d all night and a second day; the creek continued to rise.

[2] . . . A second night, and a third day, the rain continued [po]uring. At <u>dusk</u> of the third day, the water began to enter the [ho]use. **[3]** A young <u>matron</u>, wife of Don Carmen . . . told her [h]usband to take her to higher ground. . . . Before leaving, he begged his aged father and mother to accompany him, but they laughed. "You will get all wet for nothing," they said. ". . . What if there is a little water in the house?"

. . . Don Carmen set out. . . . On reaching [his brother's] house, he told Don Florencio what had happened at the upper ranch. Hurriedly the <u>latter</u> saddled his best horse and set out to see what he could do to persuade his parents to leave their house and take to the hills.

. . . From afar off . . . he could discern the roof of the house and two people perched on it. . . . **[4]** Like most ranchmen of his time, Don Florencio could not swim. He depended on his horse to carry him across streams.

Guided Reading

1. What important information does the writer include in the first sentence?

2. What words show time order in this paragraph?

3. Which words in this paragraph show that Don Justo and his wife are stubborn?

4. Why are Don Justo and his wife on the roof of their ranch?

VOCABULARY

romantic: sentimental
abatement: stopping
poured: fell
dusk: twilight
matron: wife
latter: last mentioned

READING COMPREHENSION

____ **1.** What is the main idea of the first paragraph?
   A Don Justo and his wife were foolish to stay.
   B In 1903 the La Becerra Creek flooded.
   C The Buena Vista Ranch has a long history.
   D The most romantic flooding of La Becerra Creek was in 1878.

____ **2.** Which of the following is an opinion?
   A Three times in the history of Buena Vista Ranch, La Becerra Creek has been half a mile wide—in 1878, 1903, and 1937.
   B But the rain <u>poured</u> all night and a second day; the creek continued to rise.
   C . . . A second night, and a third day, the rain continued pouring.
   D Of course, the oldest flood is the most <u>romantic</u>.

DEVELOPING YOUR SKILLS

CHOOSING AND LIMITING A RESEARCH SUBJECT   Decide whether each
of the following subjects is *too broad* or *suitably limited* for a research report of
two to five pages.

_____ **1.** a simple way of making oatmeal cookies
     A too broad
     B suitably limited

_____ **2.** causes and effects of the different types of storms
     A too broad
     B suitably limited

_____ **3.** the history of Canada
     A too broad
     B suitably limited

_____ **4.** the most effective way of controlling termites
     A too broad
     B suitably limited

_____ **5.** famous women from 19th century England
     A too broad
     B suitably limited

_____ **6.** shoes
     A too broad
     B suitably limited

_____ **7.** feeding and care of a pet hamster
     A too broad
     B suitably limited

_____ **8.** jazz music in America, 1950s to the present
     A too broad
     B suitably limited

_____ **9.** how to make charcoal rubbings from old gravestones
     A too broad
     B suitably limited

_____ **10.** a particularly interesting Internet site
     A too broad
     B suitably limited

DEVELOPING YOUR SKILLS

CLAUSES Use word webs to help you think up subordinate and independent clauses for the following topics. Use a separate sheet of paper to finish the exercise.

1. a sunrise
2. a river flooding
3. a bird flying
4. a pony running
5. a girl winning a game

DEVELOPING YOUR SKILLS

WORKS CITED PAGE Decide whether each of the following sources for research reports is written in the correct format.

_____ **1.** New York Times, The. Wilford, John Noble. "Another Meteorite May Show Life on Mars, Scientists Report." 19 March 1999, sec. A: 4.
   A correct
   B incorrect

_____ **2.** Bradbury, Ray, Arthur C. Clarke, Bruce Murray, Carl Sagan, and Walter Sullivan, Mars and the Mind of Man. New York: Harper & Row, 1973.
   A correct
   B incorrect

_____ **3.** Hefner, Alan G. "Atlantis: the Myth." Encyclopedia Mythica. 1999. <http://www.pantheon.org/mythica/articles/a/atlantis.html>
   A correct
   B incorrect

_____ **4.** Fuller, Graham. October 2000 Interview Magazine. "Tigerland's Tigers."
   A correct
   B incorrect

_____ **5.** Sally Hobart Alexander. Taking Hold: My Journey into Blindness. New York: Simon & Schuster, 1995.
   A correct
   B incorrect

_____ **6.** Carr, Michael H. "Mars." Encyclopedia Americana. 1999 ed.
   A correct
   B incorrect

_____ **7.** Kaplan, Karen. <http://www.prodworks.conVIatimes11899.html> "High-Tech Tools Give Disabled the Senses of Accomplishment."
   A correct
   B incorrect

_____ **8.** Understanding Depression. Donald F. Klein, M.D. & Paul H. Wender, M.D. New York. Oxford University Press, 1993.
   A correct
   B incorrect

_____ **9.** "Trace Your Family Tree." Good Housekeeping Oct. 1976: 240.
   A correct
   B incorrect

_____ **10.** Rev. of Schindler's List, dir. Steven Spielberg. Movie Magazine 17 March 1996: 7–10.
   A correct
   B incorrect

LIMITING A RESEARCH SUBJECT AND DEVELOPING A THESIS
Imagine that you are to write a research report on each of the areas listed
below. Without doing any actual research, limit the broad subject and write
a working thesis that establishes the purpose and main idea of the report
and helps organize the information that will follow in the report. For this
exercise, the details can be from your imagination. Use a separate sheet of
paper if necessary.

COMPOSITION

ADVANCED

1. desserts

_____
_____
_____

2. school sports

_____
_____
_____

3. cats

_____
_____
_____

4. rock, rap, or country music

_____
_____
_____

5. a particular national park in America

_____
_____
_____

▶ PROCESS OF WRITING AN I-SEARCH PAPER ON A CULTURAL TRADITION

VOCABULARY

research report: a factual essay based on information drawn from different sources

summarize: to write information in a compact manner, listing only the main ideas

working thesis: a statement that expresses a possible main idea for a paper

main topic: the main subject of a paper

subtopic: a lesser subject related to the main subject

supporting points: ideas that support your topic

supporting details: facts that support your ideas

parenthetical citation: citing a source in parenthesis in a paper

works cited page: list of all the sources used in a paper

A Writer Writes (pages C567–C568)

Purpose: to inform and explain a cultural tradition
Audience: your teacher and classmates

BASIC/INTERMEDIATE

Choose a cultural tradition that you think is interesting. Find resources in the library or in your community and write an essay explaining the tradition and what you think about it. Be sure to say what purpose the tradition serves in the culture and why you think it is interesting.

Purpose: to inform and explain a cultural tradition
Audience: your teacher and classmates

ADVANCED

Choose a cultural tradition that you think is interesting. Find resources in the library or in your community and write an essay explaining the tradition and what you think about it. Be sure to state how and why the tradition came to be important to the culture. Also include your reasons for finding this tradition interesting.

PROCESS OF WRITING AN I-SEARCH PAPER ON A CULTURAL TRADITION

1. Freewrite for five minutes about the tradition.

2. Make a list of the ideas from your freewriting and organize them from most interesting to least. Use the top three most interesting ideas.

3. Use the graphic below to help you organize your ideas.

Cultural Tradition that I find interesting

Background of tradition

Purpose of tradition

What I think about tradition

Conclusion

LETTERS AND APPLICATIONS **CHAPTER 13**

COMPOSITION

▶ GUIDED READING

Read the passage and answer the questions that follow.

FROM *Letters of A Woman Homesteader,*
by Elinore Rupert Stewart

Dear Mrs. Coney,

Are you thinking I am lost, like the Babes in the Wood? Well, I am not. . . . I am way up close to the Forest Reserve of Utah, within half a mile of the line, sixty miles from the railroad. I was twenty-four hours on the train and two days on the stage, and oh, those two days! The snow was just beginning to melt and the mud was about the worst I ever heard of. **[1]**

The first stage we <u>tackled</u> was just about as <u>rickety</u> as it could be and I had to sit with the driver, who was a Mormon and so handsome that I was not a bit <u>offended</u> . . . especially when he told me that he was a <u>widower</u> Mormon. **[2]** But, of course, as I had no <u>chaperone</u> I looked very fierce (not that that was very difficult with the wind and mud as allies) and told him my actual opinion of Mormons in general and particular.

. . . I have a very, very comfortable situation and Mr. Stewart is absolutely no trouble, for as soon as he had his meals, he retires to his room and plays on his bagpipe, only he calls it his "bugpeep." **[3]** It is "The Campbells are Coming," without <u>variations</u>, at <u>intervals</u> all day long and from seven till eleven at night. Sometimes I wish they would make haste and get here.

There is a saddle horse especially for me and a little shotgun with which I am to kill sage chickens. We are between two trout streams, so you can think of me as being happy when the snow is through melting and the water gets clear.

Guided Reading

1. How did the weather affect her journey?

2. What details show that the trip by stagecoach was difficult?

3. Why do you think Mr. Stewart pronounces "bagpipe" this way?

VOCABULARY

tackled: took on
rickety: shaky
offended: affronted
widower: a man whose wife has died
chaperone: guardian
variations: changes
intervals: different times

READING COMPREHENSION

_____ **1.** What is the author's main idea in writing the letter?
   A To tell a friend about her travels and new situation.
   B To complain about the difficulty of stagecoach travel.
   C To brag about her wonderful new life.
   D To convince her friend to move to Utah.

_____ **2.** Based on the tone of story, the author is probably ▪.
   A optimistic
   B depressed
   C pessimistic
   D bad-humored

Copyright © Barrett Kendall Publishing. All rights reserved.

Chapter 13 Letters and Applications • Level I COMPOSITION **81**

WRITING LETTERS Decide whether each of the following salutations is for a *friendly letter* or a *business letter*.

BASIC

____ **1.** Dear Aunt Margot
   A friendly letter
   B business letter

____ **2.** Dear Mr. Smith
   A friendly letter
   B business letter

____ **3.** Dear Sir or Madam
   A friendly letter
   B business letter

____ **4.** Dear Nelly
   A friendly letter
   B business letter

____ **5.** Dear Mr. President
   A friendly letter
   B business letter

____ **6.** Dear Dad
   A friendly letter
   B business letter

____ **7.** Dear Cousin Bob
   A friendly letter
   B business letter

____ **8.** Dear Mrs. Swanson
   A friendly letter
   B business letter

____ **9.** Dear Executive
   A friendly letter
   B business letter

____ **10.** Dear Naho
   A friendly letter
   B business letter

DEVELOPING YOUR SKILLS

WRITING LETTERS   Imagine that you need to write letters to each of the following people. Use the chart below to help you figure out if each one will be a business or personal letter.

1. the Mayor of your city

2. the editor of your local newspaper

3. your favorite aunt

4. your best friend

5. your favorite teacher

Person	Relationship to you	Type of letter
1.		
2.		
3.		
4.		
5.		

COMPOSITION

DEVELOPING YOUR SKILLS

BUSINESS LETTERS   Business letters are more formal than friendly letters and require a more precise form. For each of the following, pick the best answer in regards to writing business letters.

INTERMEDIATE

_____ **1.** The best paper for writing a business letter is:
   A beige, 4 x 6 inches
   B white, 8½ x 11 inches

_____ **2.** In a business letter, the inside address is:
   A the address of the business you are writing.
   B another address where you can be reached.

_____ **3.** The salutation of a business letter should go:
   A at the top of the page, before the inside address.
   B one line below the inside address.

_____ **4.** The body of a business letter starts:
   A one line below the salutation.
   B one line above the salutation.

_____ **5.** A good closing for a business letter is:
   A Very truly yours.
   B Talk to you later.

_____ **6.** In a business letter you should type your name
   A above your signature.
   B below your signature.

_____ **7.** The return address on a business envelope should go:
   A on the back of the envelope.
   B in the upper left-hand corner of the front of the envelope.

_____ **8.** If you do not know the name of the person to whom you are writing a business letter, you should use:
   A Dear Sir or Madam.
   B Dear Whoever.

_____ **9.** When you are writing a business letter it is best to:
   A make sure it is neat and clearly written.
   B make sure you had fun writing it.

_____ **10.** Whenever possible, a business letter should have a margin of:
   A at least 5 inches.
   B at least 1 inch.

DEVELOPING YOUR SKILLS

WRITING LETTERS   The following headings contain errors in
capitalization and punctuation. Write the correct versions of the headings
on the lines provided.

ADVANCED

1. 1704 milton Manor _____

  Springfield, ca 90210 _____

2. mr. Gary Scraves _____

  Maps unlimited _____

  1528 Montgomery street _____

  Seattle, WA 98141 _____

3. sincerely_____

  Betty Smith _____

4. march 11 2000 _____

5. 1421 Dere Road apartment 2C _____

  jersey city new jersey _____

VOCABULARY

modified block form: a letter where the heading,
  closing and signature are on the right

heading: your address

inside address: the address of the business you
  are writing

salutation: greeting

body: main message of your letter

closing: a word or group of words that ends
  your letter

signature: your name signed at the bottom
  of a letter

COMPOSITION

▶ GUIDED READING

Read the passage and answer the questions that follow.

FROM *Address to A Town Hall Audience, Los Angeles, 1992*, by Antonia C. Novello

I accepted the job as Surgeon General because our citizens must have the facts—as Cervantes said, we cannot "Mince the matter." [1] I am dedicated to the proposition that we must give our people the health information they need to make vital health choices and decisions that will ripple out for years to come.

As Surgeon General of the U.S. Public Health Service, I serve as the Surgeon General for all the people of the United States. When I was appointed, I didn't focus on being a woman or a minority—although I realized that in terms of an appointment, each of these characteristics was symbolic.

In my efforts to protect our nation's health, I have spoken out especially about the dangers associated with illegal underage drinking, smoking, AIDS, and violence. What I have learned since taking on this task has alarmed me, but at the same time, it has also taught me that my efforts cannot let up.

. . . The America of today is far different from what it was when we were young. The challenges are different, the pressures greater, the poverty and despair more rampant, and the availability of drugs and alcohol more widespread. These things are tragic—and we must do everything we can to turn them around. [2]

Guided Reading

1. What idea does this quotation support?

2. Based on the details in this paragraph, what do you think is the speaker's attitude toward today's America?

VOCABULARY

dedicated: committed
proposition: proposal
appointed: chosen
rampant: uncontrolled

READING COMPREHENSION

____ **1.** What is the main idea of the speech?
   A America needs to provide care for each of its citizens.
   B Women and minorities have greater health risks than most Americans.
   C Being Surgeon General is not easy.
   D Americans should care more about women and minorities.

____ **2.** Based on the speech, what do you think is the author's point of view regarding the condition of America today?
   A The problems facing America today are greater than they were in the past.
   B America is a super nation as well as a superpower.
   C Americans need to work harder in order to get ahead.
   D America has fewer problems today than it did in the past.

 **DEVELOPING YOUR SKILLS**

CHOOSING AND LIMITING A SUBJECT   Decide whether each of the
following subjects is *too broad* or *suitably limited* for a ten-minute speech.

____ **1.** poets and poetry
  A too broad
  B suitably limited

____ **2.** female singers that are popular in America today
  A too broad
  B suitably limited

____ **3.** a particularly interesting and worthwhile program on public television
  A too broad
  B suitably limited

____ **4.** recipes that everyone can enjoy
  A too broad
  B suitably limited

____ **5.** ways to research family trees on the Internet
  A too broad
  B suitably limited

____ **6.** the great life of Leonardo da Vinci
  A too broad
  B suitably limited

____ **7.** secret strategies for winning at ping pong
  A too broad
  B suitably limited

____ **8.** ways to protect yourself from sunburn this coming summer
  A too broad
  B suitably limited

____ **9.** things to do to help the onset of pet allergies
  A too broad
  B suitably limited

____**10.** the history of the state of Arkansas
  A too broad
  B suitably limited

Developing Your Skills

STRATEGIES FOR LISTENING—CHART **Use the chart below to categorize the following strategies for listening as either *verbal* or *nonverbal*.** BASIC

1. Pay attention to words like *first, most importantly* and *finally*.

2. Notice changes in pace, rhythm and intonation.

3. Pay attention to gestures and pauses.

4. Watch for changes in the speaker's body language.

5. Determine whether the speaker's attitude is positive or negative.

COMPOSITION

Strategy	Verbal	Nonverbal
1.		
2.		
3.		
4.		
5.		

DEVELOPING YOUR SKILLS

STRATEGIES FOR LISTENING—RECOGNIZING APPEALS

In order to convince an audience of a certain point, speakers will make appeals. A *bandwagon appeal* is an invitation to do or think the same thing as everyone else. A *testimonial* is a statement, usually given by somebody famous, in support of a candidate, product or movement. A *generalization* is a conclusion based on many facts and examples.

Determine whether each of the following statements is a *bandwagon appeal, testimonial,* or *generalization.*

____ **1.** Join the KIXY generation!
   A bandwagon appeal
   B testimonial
   C generalization

____ **2.** As a mother of five, I can say with complete assurance that Kid Kars are lifesavers!
   A bandwagon appeal
   B testimonial
   C generalization

____ **3.** All women must vote for our candidate.
   A bandwagon appeal
   B testimonial
   C generalization

____ **4.** Video games promote violence.
   A bandwagon appeal
   B testimonial
   C generalization

____ **5.** As a professional golfer, I know the difference GolfPro makes.
   A bandwagon appeal
   B testimonial
   C generalization

____ **6.** All democrats should support this bill.
   A bandwagon appeal
   B testimonial
   C generalization

____ **7.** Be a charter cheddar member! Join Cheddar Chums today!
   A bandwagon appeal
   B testimonial
   C generalization

____ **8.** This is Ted Grange of the Toronto Turncoats urging you to join this movement.
   A bandwagon appeal
   B testimonial
   C generalization

____ **9.** All across the nation kids are joining Kids Alert.
   A bandwagon appeal
   B testimonial
   C generalization

____ **10.** Genetically engineered foods are dangerous.
   A bandwagon appeal
   B testimonial
   C generalization

DEVELOPING YOUR SKILLS

STRATEGIES FOR LISTENING—GLITTERING GENERALITIES

Glittering Generalities are words or phrases that pack an emotional wallop. They are used to trick people into feeling positively about a subject. Glittering generalities include words associated with virtue and goodness. A speaker may try to manipulate your attitude toward a controversial idea by associating it with one of these virtue words. Some sample words are *democracy, freedom, values, family, moral,* and *motherhood.*

An example of a glittering generality is: *"In order to keep America safe for democracy, all citizens must support this legislation."* The speaker hopes that the association of democracy with good will cause the legislation to seem good too.

Write a glittering generality for the following topics using the words indicated.

1. video games [democracy]

_____

_____

2. length of school days [freedom]

_____

_____

3. fire alarms [family values]

_____

_____

4. dinner [moral fiber]

_____

_____

5. education [motherhood]

_____

_____

▶ PROCESS OF WRITING AN ORAL INTERPRETATION

A Speaker Speaks (pages C616–C617)

Purpose: to form a group and perform a reading of a scene from *The Price*   BASIC/INTERMEDIATE
Audience: classmates and members of the local community

Form a small group and pick a scene from *The Price* to perform as a reading for your classmates. Look at the scene closely to decide what it is about and what information is important. Rehearse the reading to be sure that the meaning of the scene is clear. Perform the reading for your classmates.

Purpose: to form a group and perform a reading of a scene from *The Price*   ADVANCED
Audience: classmates and members of the local community

Form a small group and pick a scene from *The Price* to perform as a reading for your classmates. Analyze the content of the scene and discuss what information is important. Use the five **W**s and **H** (**W**ho are you? **W**hat are you saying? **W**here are you saying it? **W**hy are you saying it? **W**hy and **H**ow are you saying it?), to understand character, purpose and situation. Rehearse the reading to be sure that the meaning of the scene is clear. Perform the reading for your classmates.

COMPOSITION

PROCESS OF WRITING AN ORAL INTERPRETATION

1. Make a list of answers to the five **W**s and **H**.

2. Order your list from most important to the scene to least important.

3. Complete the word web below to help you organize your ideas.

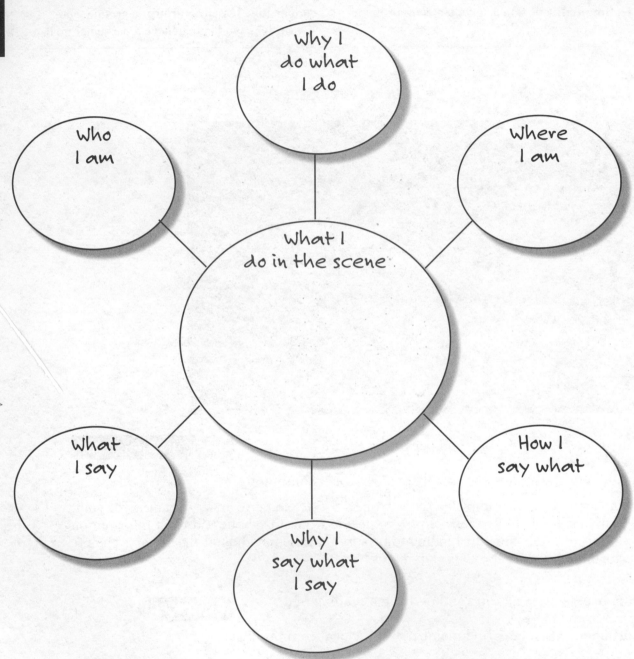

⊳ REAL-LIFE LANGUAGE

A. GIVING A PARTY

Miranda is having a party. Read Miranda's description of planning her party together with her three friends, Carlos, Jeff, and Luz. Pay special attention to the subjects in *italics* and predicates in **boldface**.

Miranda and her friends **are planning a party.** *They* **decide to have a Welcome Back to School Open House for their class.** *The party* **will be from 7 P.M. to 10 P.M. on Saturday, September 23, at the community center next door to Miranda's apartment building.**

The __(1)__ **are excited,** but *they* **can't decide what kind of party to hold.** *Jeff and Miranda* **want a dance party,** but *Luz and Carlos* **want a party with games and contests.** Finally, *the group* **agrees that the night should begin with games and contests and end with dancing.** Then, *they* **talk about music.** *Carlos* **wants rap,** but *Miranda* **points out that some people can't dance to rap.** *She* **wants salsa,** *Luz* **votes for motown and oldies,** and *Jeff* **likes rock.**

The __(2)__ **list the music choices,** __(3)__ **are the four types,** and *they* **decide to divide the time.** *Miranda, Jeff, Luz, and Carlos* **will each have one hour to play their music.**

Miranda **writes the invitations on her computer,** and __(4)__ **distributes them.** *Luz* **orders pizza, soda, and chips from her Uncle Francisco's pizzeria.** *Carlos* **borrows a sound system from his cousin.**

REAL-LIFE LANGUAGE

B. LANGUAGE SKILLS

The following sentences are from the reading passage above. Use the passage to help you choose the correct subject of the sentence.

____ **1.** The ■ are excited.
A types
B friends
C music

____ **2.** The ■ list the music choices.
A party planners
B Miranda
C Rock

____ **3.** ■ are the four types,
A salsa
B friends
C rock, rap, salsa, and oldies

____ **4.** Miranda types the invitations on her computer, and ■ distributes them.
A her
B Jeff
C the invitations

C. LANGUAGE SKILLS

Fill in the blank to complete the sentences

BASIC

____ **1.** ■ enjoy planning parties
A Patty
B Music
C Carlos and Luz

____ **2.** Her friends ■ to dance to salsa.
A Jeff, Carlos, and Luz
B like
C likes

____ **3.** ■ order about fifty pies for the pizza party.
A They
B Carlos
C The pizzeria

INTERMEDIATE

____ **4.** ■ live in the same neighborhood.
A Miranda and Luz
B Jeff
C Nearby

____ **5.** Who should ■ invite to the party?
A us
B invitations
C Miranda

____ **6.** At the party, Jeff ■ the soda.
A and Miranda
B Miranda and poured
C poured and served

ADVANCED

____ **7.** There ■ who like to play basketball.
A several people are
B are several people
C are people several

____ **7.** "■ the CD player from your cousin," suggested his mother.
A Borrow
B Borrowing
C Carlos

____ **9.** What ■ going to wear to the party?
A you
B you are
C are you

A DIFFERENT APPROACH

MEET AND GREET PARTY PLANNING [TACTILE GRAMMAR]

Materials

set of index cards, each listing a subject, such as:

He	The music	Luz
They	The pizzeria	The CD player

set of index cards, each listing a predicate, such as:

is looking forward to going to the party.	will chaperone our party.
are planning a party.	does not know what to wear to the party.
belongs to Carlos' cousin.	must be lively, and we are able to dance to it.

1. Shuffle each set of cards and place in a stack. Half of class picks subject cards.
2. The other half of the class picks predicate cards.
3. Students walk around the room trying to find a match—subject with predicate.
4. When all subjects and predicates are matched, students read sentences aloud..

> **To simplify the game:** One student chooses a subject card and the other chooses a matching predicate card. Students stand next to each other, and make a complete sentence. A third student reads the sentence.
>
> **To increase the challenge:** After students make a complete sentence, they make a question using the sentence, inverting the subject of the sentence and changing its structure.

PLAN A PARTY [ORAL GRAMMAR]

Work with three or four other students to plan a party. Follow these steps to guide you through the process.

1. Talk with the other students in the group. Make a list of all the items you need to prepare for a party.
2. Decide which students will be responsible to complete each task. Use the party planning passage you read earlier and the ideas listed below to help.
   • How many people do you plan to invite?
   • Where will you have the party?
   • How long will it be?
   • What kind of party will you have—dance, contests, picnic?
3. Make of list of each task and write the name of the student responsible for carry out that task.
4. When you are done planning, share your party plans with the class. Use your notes, but do not read them verbatim.

> **To simplify planning a party:** Each group works with an English proficient student. Student asks the group questions, and invites the ESL group to use *yes* and *no* answers or to answer in short phrases.
>
> **To increase the challenge:** Include more details in planning the party, including designing an invitation or listing the types of music or activities the group is planning.

LANGUAGE

▷ REAL-LIFE LANGUAGE

LANGUAGE

A. FAMILY

Woo gave an oral presentation about her family, who recently moved to the United States from China. Read her description, paying special attention to the proper nouns and pronouns. Proper nouns and pronouns appear in boldface.

There are four people in **my** family. **My** father is named **Ping-To Chen**. ____**(1)**____ is an electrical engineer. **My** mother is named **Wei**. ____**(2)**____ is a housewife and an artist. **My** brother, **Pi-En**, is in the sixth grade. **Everyone** calls ____**(3)**____ **Peter**. **My** name is **Woo**, and **I** have decided to keep **my** Chinese name. We came to the **United States** from **Taiwan** three years ago because **my** father's company transferred **him**. **I** am very happy to be in America, but **my** mother misses **her** family in **China**. Even though ____**(4)**____ write to **her** almost every day, **she** still misses **them**. **My** father is so busy working, **he** says **he** doesn't have time to feel lonely.

My brother loves to draw and paint like **my** mother, and **he** belongs to an after-school art club. **I** love mathematics like **my** father. On the weekends **our** family spends a lot of time together. **We** visit friends, and **my** brother and **I** go to a special Chinese school to keep up our language and Chinese education. At home, **we** speak Chinese, and **my** parents know little **English**. **They** often rely on **my** brother and **me** to help **them** with everyday chores that require speaking **English**, like shopping or answering the phone.

REAL-LIFE LANGUAGE

B. LANGUAGE SKILLS

The following sentences are from the reading passage above. Use the passage to help you choose the correct noun or pronoun for each sentence.

____ **1.** ■ is an electrical engineer.
   A Him
   B He
   C She

____ **2.** ■ is a housewife and an artist.
   A She
   B He
   C Her

____ **3. Everyone** calls ■ **Peter.**
   A her
   B he
   C him

____ **4.** Even though ■ write to **her** almost every day, **she** still misses **them**.
   A thems
   B they
   C theys

C. LANGUAGE SKILLS

Fill in the blank to complete the sentences

BASIC

____ **1.** Woo's family moved to ■.
   A the united states
   B The United States
   C the United States

____ **2.** ■ brother loves to paint and draw
   A Him's
   B Her
   C She's

____ **3.** In three years, ■ have learned to speak English fluently.
   A I
   B me
   C me's

INTERMEDIATE

____ **4.** Woo's parents want ■ children to keep up with their Chinese studies.
   A their
   B them
   C they

____ **5.** Do ■ like Chinese scroll painting?
   A everybody
   B your
   C you

____ **6.** Emigrating to America has been hardest on ■ mother.
   A they
   B he and she's
   C their

ADVANCED

____ **7.** The children learned English more easily than ■ parents did.
   A they's
   B their
   C the

____ **8.** The ■ alphabet contains more than a thousand characters.
   A Chinese
   B chinese
   C China's

____ **9.** My mother told us that in China, ■ studied calligraphy in school.
   A all of thems
   B everyones
   C everyone

LANGUAGE

A DIFFERENT APPROACH

FAMILY TREE   [TACTILE GRAMMAR]

Materials

set of index cards, each listing a family member, such as

mother	uncle	sister	brother
father	aunt	cousin	

set of index cards, each listing a pronoun, such as

he	I	they	our	him	everyone	us		whom
she	my	you	this	her	their	we		these

1. Make the set of cards, described above.

2. Divide into small groups of 5 or 6 of varying levels of English proficiency.

3. Distribute the cards of family members, one per student. Students assume the role of the person on the card.

4. Distribute the pronoun cards, 2 or 3 per group.

5. Students make up sentences using the pronouns that describe the relationship among the family members. For example, *"She is my mother." "I am her son." "These are our children."*

> **To simplify the game:** Students respond to questions using simple phrases or *yes* and *no* answers. For example, the teacher asks, *"Are you Paulo's mother?"* The student answers, *"Yes, his mother."*
>
> **To increase the challenge:** Students make up a brief history about their family. Using pronouns, they explain, for example, what each member does, where they came from, how long they have lived in America.

WHO IS YOUR FAMILY   [ORAL GRAMMAR]

Bring in a picture of your family, or draw a picture of them. You can also make collage using pictures from magazines that describes what your family is like, what you think is important to know about them.

1. Prepare an oral presentation about your family. Practice with a partner in class before your speak before the class.

2. Plan what to say. Write down five or six questions you think you should answer in your talk. Use Woo's presentation and the ideas below to help.
   • What country did you come from?
   • What kind of work does the adults in your family do?
   • How many people are in your family?

3. After you've rehearsed your talk with your partner, include the answers to any questions he or she may have about your family.

4. When giving your presentation, try not to read the questions and answers. Speak as if you are telling a story.

> **To simplify your family presentation:** Work with an English proficient student to help prepare your talk. Use simple phrases to explain your ideas.
>
> **To increase the challenge:** Interview an older family member, asking him or her about the experience of emigrating to a new country as an adult. Share what your learned about your relative's experiences with the class.

LANGUAGE

REAL-LIFE LANGUAGE

A. GIRLS PLAYING BASKETBALL

Nafi and Martina are on the school's varsity basketball team. Read the article in the school newspaper about their spectacular victory, paying special attention to the verbs. Verbs appear in boldface.

Last Wednesday, the Redbirds of Marymount High School **won** the season's opening basketball game against the Jaguars of Blueridge High School, 57–43. Nafi Phillips ___(1)___ herself to be a key player. She **ran** fast, **understood** the importance of passing and, as a result, **scored** 25 points. She **dribbled, jumped** and **shot** with grace and ease. Martina Ortiz, another excellent Redbirds player, **made** all of her foul shots and **scored** 15 points. The team's defense was strong, and they **guarded** their opponents well. In addition, the Redbirds ___(2)___ well, and they **shot** easy lay ups throughout the game. Martina **led** the team with 12 rebounds. During the game, Nafi **ran** by her opponent several times, **jumped** up and **dunked** the ball in the basket. Nafi and Martina ___(3)___ best friends, and you **can find** them practicing every afternoon for two hours after school. They **play** hard, but because they **enjoy** it, spectators ___(4)___ that they **are having** fun on the court.

B. LANGUAGE SKILLS

The following sentences are from the reading passage above. Use the passage to help you choose the correct verb for each sentence.

____ **1.** Nafi Phillips ■ herself to be a key player.
    A prove
    B proved
    C is shown

____ **2.** In addition, the Redbirds ■ well.
    A passed and rebounded
    B passing and rebounding
    C passes and rebounded

____ **3.** Nafi and Martina ■ best friends.
    A is
    B am
    C are

____ **4.** Spectators ■ that they are having fun on the court.
    A is seeing
    B can see
    C can seen

C. LANGUAGE SKILLS

Fill in the blank to complete the sentences

BASIC

____ **1.** The girls ■ basketball everyday.
    A practices
    B is practicing
    C practice

____ **2.** When Nafi's mother was in high school, she also ■ basketball.
    A was played
    B played
    C plays

____ **3.** Most people ■ that shooting baskets wins the game.
    A think
    B thinks
    C is thinking

INTERMEDIATE

____ **4.** ■ that defense is the secret to success on the court?
    A Do you realize
    B You realize do
    C Were you realizing

____ **5.** What ■ rebounding the ball mean?
    A do
    B was
    C does

____ **6.** I ■ basketball when I was in junior high school.
    A was used to play
    B used to be playing
    C used to play

ADVANCED

____ **7.** We ■ up and down the court ten times.
    A runned
    B ran
    C was running

____ **8.** The coach thought that the team ■ the game.
    A should have won
    B should have winned
    C should won

____ **9.** If you ■ free tomorrow, let's practice that lay up.
    A be
    B is
    C are

LANGUAGE

A DIFFERENT APPROACH

MATCHING BASKETBALL VERBS   TACTILE GRAMMAR

Materials

set of index cards, each listing a verb associated with basketball, such as

run	dribble	jump	bounce
guard	rebound	leap	travel
shoot	foul	practice	fall

sports magazines with pictures of people playing basketball

1. Form group of three and choose one card and one magazine.

2. As a group, look through magazines and find pictures that illustrate the verb on the card.

3. Groups write sentences using the verb as an action verb, with a helping verb, and in a verb phrase.

4. Each group shares their sentence with the class.

> **To simplify the activity:** Groups write one sentence using the verb as an action verb.
>
> **To increase the challenge:** Think of synonyms for the verbs and write sentences using the synonyms.

PLAYING BASKETBALL IN SLOW MOTION   ORAL GRAMMAR

Pretend you are either playing or announcing a basketball game. Follow these steps to guide you through the process.

1. Divide into groups of seven students. Decide who will be the players, what positions they will play, and who will be the announcer.

2. Since this is a performance, plan what your group will do. Write down 5 or 6 plays that your group wants to enact. Use the article about Nafi and Martina you read earlier and the ideas below to help.

- Limit your game to 10 plays. List 10 moves players can make, such as foul shot, rebound, hook shot, lay up.

- Think of how you would describe these moves in words and write down your thoughts.

- Is the game your group planning suspenseful? With three minutes left on the shot clock, does one team make a basket and will the game?

3. Write a list of what happens and what each player does during the game.

4. Enact the game in slow motion, so that the announcer can keep up with the moves of the team. If you are the announcer, try not to read your notes. Speak clearly so that both the audience and the players can understand you.

> **To simplify the game:** An English proficient student explains 4 basic plays, while ESL students act them out.
>
> **To increase the challenge:** After the game, interview the players, asking them about the strong and weak moments in the game.

LANGUAGE

► REAL-LIFE LANGUAGE

A. MAKING ART

Leyla and her advisor, Mr. Kantor, talked about Leyla's favorite class, Art. Read their conversation, paying special attention to the adjectives and adverbs. Adjectives and adverbs appear in boldface.

MR. KANTOR:	Why is Art your **favorite** class? You are a ___(1)___ artist.
LEYLA:	Thank you, Mr. Kantor. I ___(2)___ do enjoy painting and drawing. Whenever I am making art, I feel **so calm** and **focused**.
MR. KANTOR:	That's **interesting**. What do you mean?
LEYLA:	It is **slightly difficult** for me to explain. Perhaps, that is why I feel **more comfortable** drawing and painting what I feel rather than trying to describe them in words. But, **basically**, I respond **strongly** to color, shape, and texture.
MR. KANTOR:	Give me an example. Talk about making a drawing of flowers.
LEYLA:	In Art, when I sit down at my easel with my box of **pastel** chalk, I find myself concentrating **fully** on the subject we are drawing. I look at the vase of flowers before me, and am inspired by the ___(3)___ shades of red, purple, blue, green.
MR. KANTOR:	What do you do next?
LEYLA:	If the flowers are ___(4)___ **large**, like a sunflower, I decide whether to paint a picture of the flowers in the vase on the table or to focus on just the **enormous** flower itself. I decide whether to use **thick** or **thin** lines, blend the colors together or **carefully** draw every detail.

REAL-LIFE LANGUAGE

B. LANGUAGE SKILLS
The following sentences are from the reading passage above. Use the passage to help you choose the correct adjectives and adverbs for each sentence.

____ **1.** You are a ■ artist.
  A wonder
  B wonderful
  C wondfully

____ **2.** I ■ do enjoy painting and drawing.
  A really
  B real
  C for sure

____ **3.** I look at the vase of flowers before me, and am inspired by the ■ shades of red, purple, blue, green.
  A delicately
  B delicate
  C really

____ **4.** If the flowers are ■ large, like a sunflower, I decide whether to paint a picture of the flowers in the vase on the table.
  A real
  B way
  C very

C. LANGUAGE SKILLS
Fill in the blank to complete the sentences.

BASIC

____ **1.** Leyla told Mr. Kantor about her ■ class.
  A favoritely
  B most favorite
  C favorite

____ **2.** Artists observe ■ detail.
  A very
  B every
  C mostly the

____ **3.** After class, Leyla ■ put her art supplies away.
  A carefully
  B careful
  C caring

INTERMEDIATE

____ **4.** ■, Leyla noticed a small ladybug on the leaf of the flower.
  A Suddenly
  B Sudden like
  C Sudden

____ **5.** The artist drew the bug as part of the drawing, ■ glancing down at her paper.
  A but not once
  B hard
  C hardly

____ **6.** Why was Mr. Kantor ■ interested in hearing Leyla explain her feelings about drawing and painting?
  A so much
  B much
  C so

ADVANCED

____ **7.** The painter moved the paintbrush ■ across the canvas.
  A up and forth
  B back and forth
  C backwardly and forwardly

____ **8.** Artists ■ pay attention to the texture and shape of the object they are drawing.
  A also
  B look to
  C in addition to

____ **9.** For some people, drawing and painting is a particularly ■ experience.
  A absorbingly
  B absorbed
  C absorbing

A DIFFERENT APPROACH

PANTOMIME PICTURES TACTILE GRAMMAR

Materials

set of props, such as:

    a colorful hat   a chair
    a bouquet of fake flowers   a boot
    a sheet

1. Pairs of volunteers stand in front of the class.
2. One student pretends to pose, while the other pretends to paint, draw, or sculpt the student model. The model should use props.
3. The other class members describe the way the artist is making art and describe how the model is posing. Students should use vivid adjectives and adverbs and write those words on the board.

> **To simplify the game:** Students identify the objects or movements by answering *yes* or *no* to pointed questions, such as *"Is Immi wearing a blue hat?" "Did Ramone suddenly change his pose?"*
>
> **To increase the challenge:** Students describe the scene of the artist and model with as many details as they can observe. Students should use their imaginations, giving names and imaginary location to the participants, such as *"Pablo Picasso, the extremely brilliant artist, is painting the portrait of the ravishing Countess Alsman of Austria. She is wearing. . ."*

PORTRAIT DRAWINGS ORAL GRAMMAR

Work in small groups to create a portrait of your classmate. Follow these steps to guide you through the process.

1. Decide who you would like to draw. Talk among the students in your group.
2. Decide whether you want to draw each other or one member of your group will pose for the rest.
3. Spend five minutes drawing. Then talk about how you felt while you were posing or creating your portrait. Use the conversation you read earlier and the ideas below to help.
- Did you feel focused or distracted?
- Did you decide to concentrate on the face or did you include the whole body of your subject?
- Were your lines soft and sketchy or bold and dark?
4. Share the drawings of your group with the class. Answer any questions students from other groups might have, and be sure to ask questions about the experience other had while drawing a portrait.

> **To simplify drawing a portrait:** After drawing the portrait, point out each body part you can identify and think of an adjective or adverb that describes that part.
>
> **To increase the challenge:** Compare your experience with another class member. This person does not have to be a member of the original group. What was enjoyable about drawing? What did each of you find frustrating? Find three things in each other's drawing that you liked.

LANGUAGE

▷ REAL-LIFE LANGUAGE

A. PETS

Bettina went to the pet store to buy several items for her new puppy. Read her conversation with Mrs. Ott, the owner of the store, paying close attention to prepositional phrases, conjunctions and interjections. Prepositional phrases are in bold, conjunctions are in italics, and interjections are underlined.

MRS. OTT: Good morning, how may I help you?

BETTINA: I just got a puppy for my birthday, *and* I need to buy several things for him. First, I need some canned *and* dry food for him.

MRS. OTT: Would you like to use a shopping cart? They are ___(1)___ .

BETTINA: Okay, I'll put those five cans of dog food **in my shopping cart**. I also need two bowls, one for food *and* the other for water.

MRS. OTT: I would not buy plastic bowls. I think metal bowls **on the bottom shelf** will last longer.

BETTINA: Do you carry vitamins? The veterinarian suggested ___(2)___ I give my puppy, Esmeralda, vitamins every day, ___(2)___ I bring him to the vet more often for a check up.

MRS. OTT: I'll give you a small bottle to start *but* be sure to refill it next month.

BETTINA: *Not only* do I need vitamins, *but* I *also* need a leash and collar?

MRS. OTT: ___(3)___ We have many styles. Do you prefer a leather *or* plastic one?

BETTINA: Actually, I'll take the green leather leash ___(4)___ that is hanging **against the wall**.

B. LANGUAGE SKILLS

The following sentences are from the reading passage above. Use the passage to help you choose the correct parts of speech for each sentence.

____ **1.** Would you like to use a shopping cart? They are ■.
  A next along side the door
  B next to the door
  C against next to the door

____ **2.** The veterinarian suggested ■ I give my puppy, Esmeralda, vitamins every day, ■ I bring him to the vet more often for a check up.
  A either . . . or
  B or . . . either
  C if . . . then

____ **3.** ■ We have many styles.
  A oh
  B !Ho
  C Oh!

____ **4.** Actually, I'll take the green leather leash ■ that is hanging **against the wall**.
  A in the studded color
  B with the studded color
  C for the studded color

C. LANGUAGE SKILLS

Fill in the blank to complete the sentences

BASIC

____ **1.** ■, Bettina got a puppy.
  A for her birthday
  B from her birthday
  C For her birthday

____ **2.** ■ I would love to have a dog for a pet.
  A yes
  B Yes,
  C yes?

____ **3.** Bettina needed to buy many items for her puppy, ■ Mrs. Ott was very helpful.
  A and
  B but
  C but for

INTERMEDIATE

____ **4.** ■ Bettina found everything she needed for her new puppy.
  A At the pet store
  B On the pet store
  C During the pet store

____ **5.** Which ■ do you prefer, the yellow leash or the green leash?
  A of thems
  B of this
  C one

____ **6.** Bettina did not know what to buy, ■ Mrs. Ott helped her make the right choices for her new pet.
  A or
  B which
  C but

ADVANCED

____ **7.** Rosa wanted to buy a pet ■ she was lonely.
  A so
  B because
  C and

____ **8.** ■ pets keep people happier and healthier
  A According to many veterinarians,
  B On accounts of many veterinarians
  C In spite of many veterinarians

____ **9.** Did you choose this or ■ for your pet?
  A that
  B them
  C the one

A Different Approach

VOTING FOR FAVORITE TYPE OF PET   TACTILE GRAMMAR

Materials

set of index cards with a variety of parts of speech highlighted in the chapter, such as

Yes	in	in spite of	either . . . or
Wow	on	according to	because
Oh	next to	not only . . . but also	so

1. Shuffle the cards and place them in a stack.

2. Conduct a poll among members of the class to find out which pets students prefer. For the sake of simplicity, limit the choices to dogs, cats, mice, fish, or turtles.

3. After writing the results on the board, choose a card from the stack.

4. Work in pairs to write sentences about the poll using the parts of speech on the cards.

> **To simplify the game:** In pairs ask each other yes or no questions about the poll, using a few parts of speech listed on the cards.
>
> **To increase the challenge:** Make statements and ask questions about the results of the poll, using the parts of speech listed on the card.

SHOPPING AT THE PET STORE   ORAL GRAMMAR

Work with a partner to choose the type of pet you want to own. Follow these steps to guide you through the process of buying supplies for your new pet at the pet store:

1. Talk to your partner. Choose who will play the part of the pet owner and who will play the part of the pet store salesman.

2. Write down five or six questions that you would like to ask the salesmen about caring for your pet. Then write the salesman's answers. Use the passage about Bettina and her puppy as well as the ideas below to help you.

   • What pet did you choose. Does it live on land or in the water or both?

   • What type of food does it eat?

   • Do you need a special cage or contain to keep it in?

3. Write several questions the pet owner can ask, and record the salesman's answers.

4. When you are down planning, role-play the visit to the pet store. You can use your notes if you need to, but do not read the questions and answers aloud.

> **To simplify the game:** Have an English-proficient student play the part of the pet owner and write down those answers. Ask questions that can be answered in simple phrases.
>
> **To increase the challenge:** Research caring for the pet of your choice, so that you can include more questions and detailed answers when you role-play.

LANGUAGE

CHAPTER 6 COMPLEMENTS

▷ REAL-LIFE LANGUAGE

A. RECYCLING

Luciano makes an announcement during a meeting of the student council, encouraging students to recycle their garbage. Read his short speech, paying special attention to the direct objects, indirect objects, predicate nominatives and predicate adjectives.

In our school, there are many ways we can recycle our garbage.

Throwing out less is the first ___(1)___ to start. Every time we use a piece of paper, we can turn it over and use the other side for scrap before we throw it away. When we do throw it away, let's use the blue recycling trash container, so that we know our trash will be recycled.

The cafeteria is a great place to recycle trash. The staff has set up special trash containers students can use to sort their garbage for recycling. Look for the three garbage cans, each labeled for the specific type of garbage they hold: one for aluminum cans, one for glass containers, and one for plastic containers.

We all have to make an effort because that is the way recycling will help clean up our planet. Making an effort is very ___(2)___. To help us work together, I am starting a new student ___(3)___ called the Trashy People Club. I am inviting you to give ___(4)___ suggestions to organize a school and community wide commitment to recycling garbage. Anyone interested in becoming a Trashy Person, please see me at the end of the student council meeting.

B. LANGUAGE SKILLS

The following sentences are from the reading passage above. Use the passage to help you choose the correct complement.

_____ **1.** Throwing out less is the ■ to start.
   A first
   B first place
   C where

_____ **2.** Making an effort is very ■.
   A rewarding
   B full of reward
   C many rewards

_____ **3.** I am starting a new student ■.
   A which is
   B arrangings
   C club

_____ **4.** I am inviting you to give ■ suggestions to organize a school and community wide commitment to recycling garbage.
   A me
   B mine
   C it

C. LANGUAGE SKILLS

Fill in the blank to complete the sentences.

BASIC

_____ **1.** Recycling is ■.
   A importance
   B of important
   C important

_____ **2.** We need to give ■ a chance to survive.
   A earth
   B the earth
   C to the earth

_____ **3.** Students must be ■ to recycling.
   A committed
   B commit
   C commitment

INTERMEDIATE

_____ **4.** Some environmentalists believe that soon the oceans will be so ■ that most sea life will die.
   A polluted
   B pollute
   C pollutable

_____ **5.** Whether ■ are true remains to be seen.
   A these predicted
   B this predictings
   C these predictions

_____ **6.** I am ■ that recycling is necessary for mankind's survival.
   A clearly
   B certainty
   C certain

ADVANCED

_____ **7.** Our school's recycling efforts appear to be ■.
   A success
   B successful
   C succeed

_____ **8.** We students urge ■ to buy recycled paper products.
   A our parents
   B to our parents
   C we's parents

_____ **9.** Our school sent ■ asking him to support the recycling bill.
   A to our congressman a letter
   B our congressman to a letter
   C our congressman a letter

LANGUAGE

► A DIFFERENT APPROACH

ITEMS TO RECYCLE TACTILE GRAMMAR

Materials

a plastic soda bottle   an old newspaper
an aluminum can   an egg carton

1. Place each recyclable object on a desk at the front of the class.

2. Break into groups of three and distribute index cards, four per group.

3. Think of four everyday items you think should be recycled and write the name of the item on an index card.

4. On the other side of the index card, write a sentence using the item, either as a direct object, indirect object, predicate nominative, or predicate adjective.

5 Share your sentences with the class, stating the way the item was used in the sentence.

> **To simplify the game:** Write down the name of the everyday object and explain using short phrases the category in which the object should be recycled: plastic, metal, paper, styrofoam.
>
> **To increase the challenge:** Discuss what people should do everyday to recycle their garbage. Use the grammatical concepts discussed in your discussion.

WRITE A RECYCLING ANNOUNCEMENT   ORAL GRAMMAR

Pretend it is National Recycling Week. Work in groups of five. Vary levels of proficiency within each group. Write a short speech or announcement encouraging all students to recycle their trash.

1. Write down five or six points that the group believes are important reasons for recycling garbage. Use the announcement you read earlier and the ideas below to help.

- Why should everyone recycle his or her garbage?

- What do scientists predict will happen if we do not recycle?

- What are three immediate benefits we have experienced as a result of recycling?

2. Think about questions people who oppose recycling might ask. Think about how you would answer their questions.

3. When you are finished planning, present your announcement to the class. As you listen to the announcements prepared by other groups, write down questions you believe their announcement needs to answer.

> **To simplify making an announcement:** Present ideas in short phrases or simple declarative sentences.
>
> **To increase the challenge:** Stage a debate, one side in favor of a fully integrated recycling program; the other side more conservative, claiming that recycling is too costly and ineffective in ending the pollution of the earth.

REAL-LIFE LANGUAGE

A. CHORES

Every Saturday, Kyma helps her mother do the family's laundry. Read what she is thinking about as she hangs up the sheets on the clothes line, paying special attention to the phrases. Phrases appear in bold type.

This morning my mother and I had an argument **about doing the laundry**. Even though I know it is my job ___**(1)**___, I really do not like the chore. Because there are nine people ___**(2)**___ usually takes all morning and part of the afternoon. Every Saturday I wake up at six o'clock **to start washing clothes**. We use the **laundromat in town to wash the clothes**, but we dry most of them **by hanging them up on a clothesline in front of our house**. I felt ___**(3)**___ but this morning was especially hard. Yesterday, my friends from school invited me to go the movies, but I couldn't, which disappointed me a lot. ___**(4)**___ has a chore. My brother does the weekly food shopping, while my two older sisters dust, vacuum, and clean the house. My father does all household repairs, **like fixing the broken step on our porch**. Even my grandmother, who is seventy-five years old, helps my mother **with the cooking**.

B. LANGUAGE SKILLS

The following sentences are from the reading passage above. Use the passage to help you choose the correct phrase for each sentence.

_____ **1.** Even though I know it is my job ■, I really do not like the chore.
  A to really do the laundry
  B to do the laundry
  C doing the laundry and all

_____ **2.** Because there are nine people ■ usually takes all morning and part of the afternoon.
  A in my family, the laundry
  B the laundry in my family
  C in the laundry, my family

_____ **3.** I felt ■ but this morning was especially hard.
  A bad for my mother arguing
  B arguing with my mother bad
  C bad arguing with my mother,

_____ **4.** ■ has a chore.
  A Everyone during the week busy with school or work
  B Busy with school or work during the week, everyone
  C Busy with everyone during the week, school or work

C. LANGUAGE SKILLS

Fill in the blank to complete the sentences

BASIC

_____ **1.** Most people find chores dull but they are ■.
  A to necessary do
  B to do necessarily
  C necessary to do

_____ **2.** ■ Sheila prepares to do the week's wash.
  A To the laudromat
  B Taking a magazine to the laundromat,
  C With the laundromat and magazine

_____ **3.** The soap powder is ■.
  A on the shelf in the kitchen
  B at the shelf on the kitchen
  C the kitchen shelf

INTERMEDIATE

_____ **4.** I like ■ when I get home.
  A to cook dinner
  B cook dinner
  C cooked dinner

_____ **5.** ■ the girl asked to take a break.
  A Tired of beginning to scrubbing the floor,
  B The floor beginning to get tired of scrubbing,
  C Beginning to get tired of scrubbing the floor,

_____ **6.** ■ would like to help?
  A Which friends of you
  B One of which of your friends
  C Which one of your friends

ADVANCED

_____ **7.** ■ to carry the groceries.
  A My mother got out of the car
  B The car was parked nearby
  C There was a shopping cart

_____ **8.** Do you like to iron clothes or do you prefer ■?
  A to wear them wrinkled
  B wrinkled
  C to wrinkled wear them

_____ **9.** Having wrung out the mop, ■.
  A it was placed in the closet.
  B the boy placed it in the closet.
  C the closet door was closed.

A DIFFERENT APPROACH

CHORE CHARADES   TACTILE GRAMMAR

Materials

set of index cards, each listing a different chore, such as:

doing laundry   doing the dishes
vacuuming the carpet   making the beds
sweeping the floor   changing the linen

1. Shuffle the cards and place them in a stack.

2. A volunteer draws a card and silently acts out the chore.

4. Others guess which chore he or she is doing by asking questions. For example, *"Are you sweeping the floor?"*

5. The student who guesses the chore correctly draws the next card from the pile.

> **To simplify the game:** Use phrases and *yes* or *no* answers rather than complete sentences.
>
> **To increase the challenge:** Use examples of prepositional and infinitive phrases to describe the chores, such as *"I need to tuck in my sheets before I put on the bedspread."*

CITY AND COUNTRY CHORES   ORAL GRAMMAR

Work in small groups to think about chores people do in the city as opposed to chores people do in the country. Follow these steps to guide you through the process:

1. Talk to the members of your group. Make a list of chores that you imagine are the same and those that are different in the city and the country.

2. Write down five or six questions that might help your group. Use the ideas below if you find them useful.
   • How would chores differ if you owned your own house as opposed to renting an apartment?
   • If you lived in a large city, what types of chores might you do?
   • If you lived in the country or a remote place, how would you get your chores done?

3. Use a Venn diagram to help present your group's ideas. One circle represents city chores. The other represents country chores. In the middle, where the two circles join, write the chores shared by everyone.

4. Explain your ideas to the rest of the class.

> **To simplify the exercise:** Work with an English language proficient partner. Make three lists, one for city chores, one for country chores, and one for chores both locales share. Ask your partner to help you jot down phrases that describe the differences and similarities.
>
> **To increase the challenge:** Think about living one hundred years ago, and the types of chores you might have had to do.

LANGUAGE

▷ REAL-LIFE LANGUAGE

A. VISITING A MUSEUM

Semer and his class are visiting an art museum. Read the following discussion with the guide, paying close attention to clauses. Clauses appear in boldface.

GUIDE: **Before I begin my tour**, I like to ask students whether they prefer realistic or abstract painting?

SEMER: What is the difference between a realistic and abstract painting?

DAVID: A realistic painting uses images you can recognize ___**(1)**___ .

SEMER: Are you saying that an abstract painter does not?

GUIDE: ___**(2)**___ , you might be able to answer that question yourself.

SEMER: Am I correct in saying that the painting in the round frame, ___**(3)**___ is a realistic painting?

DAVID: I think it is realistic, in that the people look real. But I think it is a painting that shows many things, ___**(4)**___ , **who looks wealthy.**

GUIDE: That's right. The woman might have also been a famous noble woman, **who paid the artist a lot of money to paint a portrait of her and her family.**

SEMER: Now I know what you mean when you said that there is more than meets the eye in a realistic painting, **even if it looks true to life.**

REAL-LIFE LANGUAGE

B. LANGUAGE SKILLS

The following sentences are from the reading passage above. Use the passage to help you choose the correct clause for each sentence.

____ 1. A realistic painting uses images you can recognize ■.
 A because the painter makes the painting true to life
 B because of making the painting true to life
 C because is true to life

____ 2. ■, you might be able to answer that question yourself
 A If you were waiting until you looked at the painting galleries
 B If you wait until you have looked at the painting galleries
 C If you will be waiting to look at the painting galleries

____ 3. Am I correct in saying that the painting in the round frame, ■ is a realistic painting?
 A which was looking like it was painting a long time ago,
 B which looks like a painting painted from a long time ago,
 C which looks as if it was painted a long time ago,

____ 4. But I think it is a painting that shows many things, ■, who looks wealthy.
 A such as, the woman, in the middle,
 B such as the woman in the middle,
 C the woman in the middle,

C. LANGUAGE SKILLS

Fill in the blank to complete the sentences

BASIC

____ 1. The art museum was more interesting ■.
 A than it was expected to be
 B from my expectations
 C than I expected

____ 2. I like abstract paintings, ■.
 A or some like realistic ones
 B but some like realistic ones
 C where some like realistic ones

INTERMEDIATE

____ 3. I was surprised to see a sculpture by Rodin, ■.
 A whose work I love
 B that I love
 C which I love

____ 4. ■ will we have time to see the next exhibit?
 A When after we are finished,
 B After we will be seeing,
 C After we are finished,

ADVANCED

____ 5. ■, the children wandered into the hall of knights in armor.
 A While trying to find the exhibit,
 B While they will be finding the exhibit,
 C While they had be finding the exhibit,

____ 6. ■ I noticed an artist sketching a Greek statue.
 A As leaving the museum,
 B As it was time to leave,
 C As we left the museum,

A DIFFERENT APPROACH

MUSEUM MASTERPIECE MYSTERY   ⟨TACTILE GRAMMAR⟩

Materials

set of postcards of paintings, sculpture or drawing by famous artists, such as

Pablo Picasso	Rodin	Roy Lichtenstein
Jackson Pollock	Michelangelo	Seurat
Marc Chagall	Monet	

1. Divide into groups of three.

2. Each group chooses one card.

3. Write four clues, using clauses that will help other groups identify the work of art on the postcard.

4. Tape cards on the board.

5. Groups take turns presenting their clues to the class.

6. The group that guesses correctly which work of art is being described is the next one to take their turn.

> **To simplify the game:** Use phrases rather than complete sentences to give clues.
>
> **To increase the challenge:** Research a fact about the art movement that helped inspire the work of art and a fact about the artist who created the piece.

CLASSROOM MUSEUM   ⟨ORAL GRAMMAR⟩

Find an interesting photograph in a newspaper or magazine. Work with a partner to create a description of your photo for a museum tour.

1. Plan what you are going to say. Write down 5 or 6 reasons why you chose this photo.

2. Think of 3 or 4 questions people might ask you about the photo. Use the conversation you read earlier and the following ideas to help.
  • Why is this photo interesting to you?
  • Why do you like it?

3. Write down the answers to these and other questions you and your partner generate. When you are finished, rehearse your presentation with your partner.

4. Make a museum in the classroom. Pay special attention to the way you display each photo. Take turns being the tour guide as each student talks about the photo he or she chose.

> **To simplify:** Work with a more proficient partner, who helps you record your ideas in short phrases. Try not to read your notes when you tell about the photo you chose for the museum.
>
> **To increase the challenge:** Make a brochure for your museum. Invite other classes to tour the exhibit.

LANGUAGE

▶ REAL-LIFE LANGUAGE

A. CARS

Ingrid and her friends are looking at a car parked in front of their school. Read their conversation, paying special attention to sentence fragments, which appear in boldface type and run-on sentences, which are underlined.

INGRID: **Love that car.** The color is gorgeous.

CONSUELO: **Really? Not me.** The style is sleek, but the color is too flashy. Black is more sophisticated. **Maybe even navy blue.**

INDIA: You two are too much I mean, honestly, who cares what a car looks like I mean as long as it has four wheels and a working engine.

INGRID: **To each his own.** That's what I always say. I can't wait to get my driver's license.

CONSUELO: **Which is four years away.** If you had your license. What car would you get?

INGRID: I'd get a sports car. **Like this one.**

INDIA: Would your parents let you drive a car like that?

INGRID: **No way!** I'm describing a fantasy. My parents are more practical. They would make me drive around in their '89 Buick station wagon!

CONSUELO: **My dream?** I'd buy a reliable, fuel-efficient car. **A white one.**

INDIA: **Not worried that wouldn't be flashy enough for you, Connie?** Honestly, I can't believe the way you talk I mean I haven't heard one word about flashy cars!

CONSUELO: Flashy cars are a waste of money!

REAL-LIFE LANGUAGE

B. LANGUAGE SKILLS

The following sentence fragments and run-on sentences are from the reading passage above. Choose the letter of the corrected sentence.

____ **1.** Maybe even navy blue.
  A Maybe even a navy blue car.
  B Maybe, I'd like to own even a navy blue car.
  C Maybe even navy blue as the color of my car.

____ **2.** If you had your license. What car would you get?
  A If you had your license what car would you get?
  B If, for example, you had your license, what car would you get?
  C If you had your license, and what car would you get?

____ **3.** My dream?
  A The car that I drive in my dreams?
  B My car dream?
  C Do you know what my dream car is?

____ **4.** Honestly, I can't believe the way you talk I haven't heard one word about flashy cars!
  A Honestly. I can't believe the way you talk. I haven't heard one word about flashy cars!
  B Honestly, I can't believe. The way you talk I haven't heard one word about flashy cars!
  C Honestly, I can't believe the way you talk! I haven't heard one word about flashy cars!

C. LANGUAGE SKILLS

Choose the letter of the corrected sentence.

BASIC

____ **1.** Locked my keys in the car.
  A Locked my keys in the car last night.
  B Locking my keys in the car.
  C I locked my keys in the car.

____ **2.** I need an oil change my car works well.
  A I need an oil change, my car works well.
  B My car works well I need an oil change.
  C I need an oil change, but my car works well.

INTERMEDIATE

____ **3.** As I drove out the driveway.
  A As I drove out the driveway, I skidded.
  B As I drove out the driveway onto the road.
  C As I drove out the driveway in the other direction.

____ **4.** Why after looking for a new car?
  A Why after looking for a new fancy car?
  B Why after looking for a new red car?
  C Why after looking for a new car did you buy a truck?

ADVANCED

____ **5.** Do engineers design cars? To make them safe?
  A How do engineers design cars. To make them safe?
  B How do engineers design cars to make them safe?
  C How do engineers design cars making them safe?

A DIFFERENT APPROACH

....

DESIGN YOUR DREAM CAR   TACTILE GRAMMAR

Materials

> magazines, brochures, newspapers with pictures of cars
> sheets of 8½ x 11 white paper
> index cards

1. Form small groups and distribute the magazines, brochures and newspapers. Each group should take a sheet of blank paper and an index card.

2. Groups should pretend they are members of a design team, commissioned to design the car of their dreams.

3. Look through the materials to get some ideas for the cars they will be designing.

4. List on the index cards features about the dream car. Avoid run-ons and sentence fragments, and describe these sentences in full sentences.

5. Present the plans of the designed cars to the class. Use the index cards for prompts, but try not to read directly from them.

6. At the end of each presentation, ask the different presenters questions.

> **To simplify the activity:** Express ideas in short phrases or respond with *yes* or *no* answers.
>
> **To increase the challenge:** Include in the dream car plans some information on the ways their car is environmentally safe.

FANTASY DRIVING   ORAL GRAMMAR

Arrange four chairs in two rows, two chairs per row, to make a pretend car. Imagine you are taking a car trip.

1. In your group of four—one driver and three passengers—decide where you are going to go on your car trip. You also might to decide the kind of car you'll be driving.

2. Use the questions below to help you focus on your trip. Then write down 5 or 6 more questions and answers to really imagine going on the trip.
   - Where are you going? What are you bringing?
   - How long will your trip last?
   - How far is your destination? Will you be sharing the driving?

3. When you are done planning, role-play the trip. Each group gets a turn to pretend to go on a car trip. Be sure that you stop in a gas station before you "leave" to fill up the tank, and when you're on the road, buckle your seat belt.

> **To simplify fantasy driving:** Drive around the neighborhood or the school. Use phrases to tell what you are doing, such as turning the key in the ignition, honking your horn, stopping for a red light.
>
> **To increase the challenge:** Bring in some road maps and calculate the actual number of miles, the estimated time of arrival according to your calculations, and the most direct route.

LANGUAGE

▷ **REAL-LIFE LANGUAGE**

A. POLITICS/VOTING/STUDENT ELECTION

Kadatou is casting his ballot. Marisol is waiting to cast her vote behind him. Jared
has just voted. Read their conversation, paying special attention to the verbs. Verbs
appear in boldface type.

MARISOL: It's your turn. Whom **are** you **voting** for?

KADATOU: I **am** not **telling** you. The voting **is supposed** to be secret.

MARISOL: I **am voting** for Anita. She ____(1)____ my best friend. She **is running** for
Student Council President.

KADATOU: I **was going** to vote for her. But I ____(2)____ my mind. I **heard** she supports
changing the student dress code. I **do** not **support** that.

MARISOL: I **think** changing the dress code **is** important. I **think** students should not
spend so much money on clothes.

KADATOU: I **think** students **can decide** for themselves what to wear. But ____(3)____
you ____(3)____ the study hall lately? There **are** not enough tables for
everyone, and there **is** no supervision. Improving the study halls **is** the
most important issue for me.

JARED: I **was** in the study hall yesterday. There **was** nowhere to sit and everyone
was making too much noise. I **could** not **concentrate**.

MARISOL: Then you **voted** for the candidate who **is promising** to improve the study
halls?

JARED: I **cast** my ballot for the candidate who ____(4)____ all the students' needs, in
my opinion.

LANGUAGE

B. LANGUAGE SKILLS

The following sentences are from the reading passage above. Use the passage to help you choose the correct verb for each sentence.

____ **1.** She ■ my best friend.
   A will be
   B is
   C is being

____ **2.** But I ■ my mind.
   A have changed
   B will have changed
   C was changing

____ **3.** But ■ you ■ the study hall lately?
   A are . . . seeing
   B did . . . saw
   C have . . . seen

____ **4.** I cast my ballot for the candidate who ■ all the students' needs in the future.
   A will represent
   B was representing
   C has represented

C. LANGUAGE SKILLS

Choose the letter of the correct verb that completes each sentence.

BASIC

____ **1.** I ■ for Roberto Jones.
   A voted
   B vote
   C had voting

____ **2.** He ■ in representing all of the students.
   A believe
   B was believed
   C believes

____ **3.** In his speech last week, he ■ to make the school a better, safer environment where all students can learn.
   A promises
   B will promise
   C promised

INTERMEDIATE

____ **4.** ■ you ■ the debate between Roberto and Antonia?
   A Did ... heard
   B Have ... hear
   C Did ... hear

____ **5.** Antonia ■ about the problems in the cafeteria.
   A will have talk
   B was talking
   C will have talking

____ **6.** She ■ a clear stand on raising environmental issues with the administration.
   A tooked
   B will have took
   C took

ADVANCED

____ **7.** Roberto has an excellent record. For many years, he ■ English to foreign-language students.
   A taught
   B has been taught
   C teached

____ **8.** Lately, he ■ incoming students on how to choose their classes.
   A advises
   B advised
   C has been advising

____ **9.** Antonia's experience as an assistant basketball coach ■ her understand the problems of high school athletes.
   A will have helped
   B will be helping
   C will help

LANGUAGE

A DIFFERENT APPROACH

. . . .

TALKING ABOUT VOTING   TACTILE GRAMMAR

Materials

A current calendar

1. Circle today's date on the calendar.

2. Have a volunteer write the following on the board: *vote, voted, will vote, am voting, was voting, will be voting, have voted, had voted, will have voted.* Have the volunteer also write the following words on the board: *today, yesterday, last week, tomorrow*

3. The volunteer points to today's date and asks class: *Have you already voted today?* Class answers: *Yes, I have already voted,* or *No, I have not already voted.* The volunteer points to a date in the past and asks: *Did you vote last Thursday?* Class answers: *Yes, or, no, I did/did not vote last Thursday,* or *Yes, no, I voted last Thursday.* Go around the class until everybody has had a chance to answer a question.

> **To simplify the game:** Work with the simple tenses only: past, present and future.
>
> **To increase the challenge:** Add an event to each sentence to show the relationship of the two events with the tenses, such as: *Before I went to school last Thursday, I voted.*

CONDUCT A VOTE   ORAL GRAMMAR

Materials

Index cards, shoe box

1. Choose an issue to vote on such as: Should there be more homework? Who will win the World Series? or any other question.

2. Use a shoebox with a hole in it for a ballot box. Each student writes his or her choice on the index cards, and casts their votes in the ballot box.

3. Have a volunteer count up the votes and announce the results.

4. After voting process is complete, discuss the voting process.

> **To simplify the conversation:** Have an English-proficient student conduct the questions, asking the class about how they voted. Questions should be answered in simple phrases.
>
> **To increase the challenge:** Include references to other events in the day, both before and after the vote, such as *Did you vote before coming to class?*

▶ REAL-LIFE LANGUAGE

A. PROFESSIONAL BASKETBALL

Marc and Kim are watching a basketball game on television. Read the conversation that follows, and pay special attention to the use of pronouns. Pronouns appear in boldface type.

Marc and Kim are watching a college basketball game on TV. **It** is very exciting. __(1)__ team is down by three points, and **it** is the fourth quarter.

"Look at that great jumpshot Number 14 took!" said Marc. "**He** is **their** star player."

"Did **you** see how **he** stole that ball from __(2)__?" Kim interrupted, pointing to the television.

"**I** think the only chance **we** have is a three-point shot to tie the game," said Kim.

"But first **we** will have to get the ball back," said Marc.

"Can you believe **it**? How could the referee miss such an obvious double dribble?"

"**He** must be asleep on his feet," said Kim. "Hey, Marc, would you pass __(3)__ the popcorn?"

"Here, catch. Did **you** see that? Now **they** are tied! There are only 30 seconds left in the game. **Who** is going to win?"

"Look, number 14 is coming down the field. **He** is going to shoot! **It** bounced off the backboard! Look at all those people going for the rebound!"

"Number 4 got it! Now **he** is going downfield! **He** shoots! **He** makes it! The crowd is going wild!"

"**They** are going crazy!"

"**It** is over!"

"__(4)__ won!! __(4)__ team won! Victory is __(4)__!"

"**I** told **your** brother **we** would win!"

"And **he** just laughed at **you**!"

"**Who** is laughing now?"

REAL-LIFE LANGUAGE

B. LANGUAGE SKILLS

The following sentences are from the reading passage above. Use the passage to help you choose the correct pronoun for each sentence.

____ 1. ■ team is down by three points.
A They
B They're
C Their

____ 2. "Did you see how he stole that ball from ■?
A them
B their
C they

____ 3. "Would you pass ■ the popcorn?"
A I
B myself
C me

____ 4. "■ won!! ■ team won! Victory is ■!"
A Us … Us' … ours'
B We … Our … ours
C We's … Ours … our

C. LANGUAGE SKILLS

Choose the letter of the correct pronoun to complete each sentence.

BASIC

____ 1. Last week my friend and ■ decided to buy tickets for the basketball game.
A me
B myself
C I

____ 2. ■ must have waited on line for three hours.
A Us
B We
C Ourselves

____ 3. After all that, we found out that our friends had bought tickets for ■.
A us
B we
C ourselves

INTERMEDIATE

____ 4. Do you know ■ else is going?
A who
B whom
C which

____ 5. They have better seats than ■ do.
A us
B we
C ours

____ 6. I think our seats are better than ■.
A they
B they're
C theirs

ADVANCED

____ 7. The girls ■ I spoke to said they're going too.
A who
B whom
C whomever

____ 8. ■ is going will see a great game.
A Who
B Whom
C Whoever

____ 9. All of ■ should be happy we got tickets.
A us
B we
C ours

124 Chapter 11 Using Pronouns • Level I LANGUAGE

A DIFFERENT APPROACH

"HOT POTATO" TACTILE GRAMMAR

Materials

a potato or a ball

1. Divide the class into two groups. One group will play the game. One group will watch and narrate.

2. In the first group, one player passes the "hot potato" to someone else.

3. In the second group, one person names the players and makes a sentence. For example: *Juanita passes the ball to John.*

4. A second student from the observing group replaces the proper names with pronouns. For example: *She passes the ball to him.*

5. Continue until the ball has been passed all the way around the circle, or until everyone in the second group has had a chance to replace proper nouns with pronouns.

> **To simplify the game:** All students are in the playing circle. As they pass the ball from one to another, each player should say: *I pass the ball to him/her; She/he passes the ball to me;* Or, *You pass the ball to me. I pass the ball to you.*
>
> **To increase the challenge:** The playing group divides into two teams. Team members may pass the ball either as individuals, or together as a group. Observers ask the question: *Who is passing the ball to whom?* Players answer: *He/she is passing to him/her,* or, *They are passing to them.*

ANNOUNCING A BASKETBALL GAME ORAL GRAMMAR

Materials

a small ball
an empty, clean waste basket on a table

1. Four students, two boys and two girls, volunteer to be players on opposing teams. Each team has one boy and one girl.

2. Two students narrate the game from the sidelines.

3. The announcers start by naming the players who are playing this round. They can name the teams. For example: *For the Rangers today, we have Mary and Jemeel. For the Bluejays, we have Martin and Faye.*

4. When the game starts, let the announcers follow the game and report the passes and the blocks. For example: *Mary is passing to Jemeel. Martin blocks her. He steals the ball from her. Now he passes the ball to Faye. She drops it. Mary picks it up and passes it back to Jemeel.*

5. Students switch places, so that everyone gets the chance to play and announce.

> **To simplify the game:** Students first brainstorm a list of verbs relating to basketball. Write these verbs on the board. Make sentences with the verbs by adding pronouns. Practice saying these sentences aloud.
>
> **To increase the challenge:** One announcer asks questions for each play: *Who's passing to whom? Who's blocking whom?* The second announcer answers the question. Announcers should switch roles.

> ## REAL-LIFE LANGUAGE

A. GROCERY

Elijah is shopping at the supermarket. Read the narrative that follows, and pay special attention to subject-verb agreement. Subject-verb agreement appears in boldface type.

    Elijah is shopping at the supermarket. **Oranges** ___(1)___ in season. **He weighs** them and **checks** the price. Then **he checks** the list his mother gave him. **Eggplant, garlic, onions, tomatoes and carrots are** next. **All** these items ___(2)___ easy to find. **Next** on the list **is** meat. The **pork chops look** fresh, but there ___(3)___ no chicken. **He crosses** that off the list. A **package** of cheese ___(4)___ $4.98. **There is** a sale on lemonade—two quarts for the price of one. **Several people are** buying up this sale item. Now **he has** only one item left. **He does** not **know** where to find it. **A man is stocking** the shelves. **Elijah stops** to ask him where he can find spaghetti. **Spaghetti and spaghetti sauce are** in aisle four, the **man tells** him. On the way to the checkout counter, **Elijah sees** the cake counter. **Everyone** in his family **likes** cake. **He chooses** a chocolate layer cake. **Now all he has to do is** pay. **His mother will be happy** when he comes home with the shopping done.

REAL-LIFE LANGUAGE

B. LANGUAGE SKILLS
The following sentences are from the reading passage above. Use the passage to help you choose the correct verb for each sentence.

____ **1.** Oranges ■ in season.
    A are
    B is
    C have been

____ **2.** All these items ■ easy to find.
    A is
    B are
    C are being

____ **3.** The pork chops look fresh, but there ■ no chicken.
    A were
    B is
    C are

____ **4.** A package of cheese ■ $4.98.
    A costed
    B cost
    C costs

C. LANGUAGE SKILLS
Choose the letter of the correct verb form to complete each sentence.

BASIC

____ **1.** Apples and oranges ■ good snacks.
    A maked
    B make
    C making

____ **2.** Alfredo ■ been shopping three times this week already.
    A have
    B was
    C has

____ **3.** We all ■ to eat sweets sometimes.
    A loves
    B love
    C loving

INTERMEDIATE

____ **5.** Junk food ■ not good for you.
    A is
    B has been
    C are

____ **5.** The label on that package ■ it contains artificial coloring.
    A will have said
    B say
    C says

____ **6.** Do you ■ like chocolate ice cream?
    A likes
    B liking
    C like

ADVANCED

____ **7.** Every dish my mother cooks ■ my father.
    A pleases
    B is pleasing
    C please

____ **8.** Each of us ■ a favorite food.
    A have
    B has
    C has been having

____ **9.** Both Allison and her sister ■ the cooking show.
    A watches
    B watch
    C had watch

LANGUAGE

A DIFFERENT APPROACH

SHOPPING FOR GROCERIES   TACTILE GRAMMAR

Materials

Pictures from magazines or newspapers of various fruits, vegetables, and other items from a supermarket

1. One person holds up a picture and asks a second student: *Are there any apples?*

2. The second student responds, *Yes, there is one apple,* or *Yes, there are two apples*.

3. The first student takes a new picture, and questions the next student, using the same form.

4. Proceed until all the students have answered a question correctly. Then let a different student ask the question, until each student has both answered questions and asked the questions.

> **To simplify the game:** Ask: *Do you have any apples?* Have students answer the question using the following: *I, you, he, she, we, they*.
>
> **To increase the challenge:** Ask the following questions: *Did you buy any apples?*; and, *Have you bought any apples?* Answer the questions for the following: *I, you, he, she, we, they*.

ACT OUT GROCERY SHOPPING   ORAL GRAMMAR

Materials

Pictures of fruits, vegetables, and other foods and products from the supermarket

1. Sort out the pictures so that fruits are in one pile, vegetables in another, cheese and dairy products in another, etc. Label each pile: Aisle One, Aisle Two, Aisle Three, etc.

2. One person stands behind the table for each different pile of pictures (so that one person is selling fruits, another vegetables, another cheese and dairy products, for example).

3. Have the rest of the students approach the table and begin to "shop."

4. Have the shopping students frame the questions in the following way:
• *Do you have any coffee today? Are there any grapes today?*
The sellers can answer in a variety of ways:
• *Yes, I/we have coffee today. No, I don't have any coffee today, but he has coffee. Yes, there are grapes today. I don't have any grapes, but she has grapes in Aisle Two.*

5. Each time the seller and buyer complete a sentence correctly, the seller gives the buyer the picture to put in his/her shopping bag.

> **To simplify the game:** Discuss how to frame the questions, and write each "shopping question" out on the blackboard. Discuss the ways to answer each question.
>
> **To increase the challenge:** Unpack shopping bags and explain what to do with each of the "items."

▶ REAL-LIFE LANGUAGE

A. RESTAURANT

Yasmin and Julio are going to a restaurant. Yasmin's cousin, Maria, works there. Read the conversation that follows, and pay special attention to the use of adjectives and adverbs. Adjectives and adverbs appear in boldface type.

JULIO: Have you ever been here before?

YASMIN: Oh yes, this is my **favorite** restaurant. My cousin **also** works here, so we're sure to get the _____(1)_____ service!

MARIA: Hi, Yasmin, where would you like to sit?

YASMIN: Hi, Maria, this is my **good** friend, Julio. We'd like the **round** table by the **big** window.

MARIA: Sure, just follow me.

JULIO: The food looks **excellent**.

YASMIN: This is a **family** restaurant. All the food is **home-made**.

JULIO: The prices are **much more reasonable** here than they were at that **last** place we went to.

YASMIN: That was the _____(2)_____ meal I have ever had. On top of it, the food wasn't even **good**. They had the _____(3)_____ service, too.

JULIO: They also had the **loudest** music, remember? We had to shout to hear each other.

YASMIN: Who recommended that **awful** place to us?

JULIO: I read about it in the newspaper. A **restaurant** critic gave it **three** stars. He said it had a **very sophisticated** atmosphere.

YASMIN: I guess I prefer a **less sophisticated** atmosphere. Here, they have **good** food, **friendly** service, and **inexpensive** prices.

JULIO: I like this _____(4)_____, too. Shall we order? What are you going to have?

REAL-LIFE LANGUAGE

B. LANGUAGE SKILLS

The following sentences are from the reading passage above. Use the passage to help you choose the correct adjective or adverb for each sentence.

____ **1.** We're sure to get the ■ service!
   A best
   B bestest
   C most best

____ **2.** That was the ■ meal I have ever had.
   A expensivest
   B most expensivest
   C most expensive

____ **3.** They had the ■ service, too.
   A baddest
   B worst
   C most worst

____ **4.** I like this ■, too.
   A more better
   B much more better
   C much better

C. LANGUAGE SKILLS

Choose the letter of the correct adjective or adverb to complete each sentence.

BASIC

____ **1.** Yesterday, I went with my friend Janet to a ■ restaurant.
   A good
   B more good
   C better

____ **2.** They had the ■ food I have ever tasted.
   A bestest
   B most best
   C best

____ **3.** I had ■ fun than I have had in a long time.
   A the mostest
   B more
   C the more

INTERMEDIATE

____ **4.** All through dinner, we were talking about the math test. Janet said it was going to be the ■ test this semester.
   A most difficult
   B difficultest
   C most difficultest

____ **5.** Suddenly, I didn't feel ■.
   A good
   B well
   C weller

____ **6.** Then I started making the ■ jokes, and she started to laugh.
   A most silly
   B most silliest
   C silliest

ADVANCED

____ **7.** Janet is probably ■ student I know.
   A more competitive
   B most competitive
   C the most competitive

____ **8.** I told her that worrying only makes things ■.
   A worser
   B worse
   C worst

____ **9.** There is ■ I like better than having a good time with a friend.
   A anything
   B something
   C nothing

LANGUAGE

A DIFFERENT APPROACH

RESTAURANT MENU GAME   TACTILE GRAMMAR

Materials

> one large piece of poster-sized paper
> a dark marking pen

1. A volunteer asks each student, one by one, *What is your favorite food?*
2. Each student answers: *"My favorite food is. . . ."*
3. Create three lists of favorite foods, putting some students' responses in the first list, some in the second list, and some in the third list.
4. Have the students create names for three restaurants and put the names at the top of the three lists.
5. Then ask the students the following questions:
   Which is your favorite restaurant?
   Which restaurant is good?
   Is this restaurant better than that one?
   Which restaurant is the best?

> **To simplify the game:** List three things which are important in a restaurant, such as food, service, and atmosphere. The volunteer points to one of the "menus" and asks: *Is this a good restaurant?*
>
> **To increase the challenge:** Answer the following questions: *Which is the best restaurant? Which is the worst restaurant?* Use the words *best* and *worst* to describe the food, service, and atmosphere.

ACT OUT GOING TO A RESTAURANT   ORAL GRAMMAR

Work with a partner to role-play, or act out, going to a restaurant. Follow these steps to guide you through the process.

1. Talk to your partner. Choose who will play the part of the customer, and who will play the part of the waiter.
2. Plan what to say. Write down five or six questions the customer will ask, and write the waiter's answers. The questions and answers should focus on using good, better, best. Use the ideas below to help create the dialogue.
   Question: *Which table is good, the one by the window or the one by the door?*
   Answer: *The table by the window is good.*
   Question: *Which dish is better, the pork chops or the chicken?*
   Answer: *The pork chops are better than the chicken.*
3. Write several questions the waiter can ask, using comparisons, and record the customer's answers.
4. When you are done planning, role-play going to a restaurant. You can use your notes if you need to, but do not read the questions and answers aloud.

> **To simplify the game:** Have an English-proficient person record the ideas and take the part of the waiter. Ask questions that use comparisons that can be answered in simple phrases.
>
> **To increase the challenge:** Pose questions that compare one restaurant to another. Questions can also focus on the restaurants' decorations, mood, theme, and atmosphere.

> ## REAL-LIFE LANGUAGE

A. LETTER
Isabel is writing a letter to her grandmother. Read the letter that follows, paying special attention to the use of capital letters. Capitals appear in boldface type.

September 4, 2000

Dear ____(1)____randmother,

    I am sorry **I** haven't written sooner, but we have been so busy ever since we arrived here. ____(2)____ew ____(2)____ork ____(2)____ity is so big and there are so many people! **W**e have been to see many of the sights: the **E**mpire **S**tate **B**uilding, the **W**orld **T**rade **C**enter and **R**ockefeller **C**enter. **M**onday was a holiday, ____(3)____abor ____(3)____ay. **W**e all went to **C**entral **P**ark for a big family picnic. **A**ll the cousins were there, **S**ammy, **E**duardo, **J**ennifer, and **L**inda. **O**h! **I** almost forgot to tell you! **L**inda announced she is getting married at **C**hristmas! **S**he wants to have the wedding in **P**uerto **R**ico, so I guess we'll all be heading down there for the big event.

    I think **I** will like going to school here. **I** have already started. **I** am going to the ____(4)____artin ____(4)____uther ____(4)____ing ____(4)____igh ____(4)____chool. **I** like my teachers and my classes, and **I** think **I** will do very well. **I** already have a new friend there. **H**er name is **S**ara and her family comes from **P**akistan!

    I have to go now. **I** have a big test tomorrow in **A**lgebra and **I** have to study. **I** miss you and **I** will write again soon. **P**lease tell everyone hello for me, and be sure to give **M**uffin an extra dog biscuit for me.

    Love,

Isabel

Isabel

LANGUAGE

REAL-LIFE LANGUAGE

B. LANGUAGE SKILLS
The following sentences are from the reading passage above. Use the passage to help you choose the correct adjective or adverb for each sentence.

___ **1.** Dear ▪randmother,
  A grandmother
  B Grandmother
  C GrandMother

___ **2.** ▪ew ▪ork ▪ity is so big and there are so many people!
  A new York city
  B New York city
  C New York City

___ **3.** Monday was a holiday, ▪abor ▪ay
  A labor day
  B Labor day
  C Labor Day

___ **4.** I am going to the ▪artin ▪uther ▪ing ▪igh ▪chool.
  A Martin luther king high school
  B martin Luther King high School
  C Martin Luther King High School

C. LANGUAGE SKILLS
Choose the letter that shows the correct use of capital letters to complete each sentence.

BASIC

___ **1.** The last night of october is my favorite holiday, halloween.
  A October . . . halloween
  B October . . . Halloween
  C october . . . Halloween

___ **2.** This year, I'm thinking about dressing up as count dracula.
  A count Dracula
  B Count dracula
  C Count Dracula

___ **3.** My best friend wants to go as homer simpson.
  A homer Simpson
  B Homer simpson
  C Homer Simpson

INTERMEDIATE

___ **4.** We will meet on thompson st. and head down division st.
  A Thompson st. . . . Division st.
  B Thompson St. . . . Division St.
  C thompson St. . . . division St.

___ **5.** The cinema nova always has good treats for trick-or-treaters.
  A Cinema Nova
  B Cinema nova
  C cinema Nova

___ **6.** Then we pass by burger haven because he always gives out choco-puffs.
  A burger haven . . . Choco-puffs
  B burger Haven . . . choco-Puffs
  C Burger Haven . . . Choco-Puffs

ADVANCED

___ **7.** My older sister is visiting from bennington college, in vermont.
  A bennington College . . . vermont
  B Bennington college . . . Vermont
  C Bennington College . . . Vermont

___ **8.** She is studying modern art and arts administration.
  A Modern art . . . Arts administration
  B modern Art . . . arts Administration
  C Modern Art . . . Arts Administration

A Different Approach

MONUMENTS, NATURAL WONDERS, AND PLACES OF INTEREST GUESSING GAME

TACTILE GRAMMAR

Materials

detailed map of your town or city which includes places of interest
index cards

1. Identify places of interest in your area, such as buildings, museums, historic sites, or lakes, dams, rivers, parks, mountains, etc.

2. Write down the name of each place on an index card. Write clearly, in large letters. Be sure to capitalize correctly.

3. Shuffle the cards. A volunteer picks a card.

4. The volunteer gives clues about the place to other students, such as *This is a place of historic interest*, or *This is a building*, or *There is water here*.

5. Students guess the place. When they guess correctly, the volunteer holds up the card for all to see and says the name of the place.

> **To simplify the game:** Have an English proficient student draw the cards and give the clues.
>
> **To increase the challenge:** The volunteer holding the card answers the questions with a complete sentence.

WRITE A LETTER TO A FRIEND

ORAL GRAMMAR

Working with partners, conduct interviews to help identify places of interest each person has visited lately. Use the information from the interview to write a letter to your partner. Follow these steps to guide you through the process.

1. Interview your partner. Ask him or her questions about places of interest he/she has visited lately. Ask questions such as the following:
   What did you do on the weekend?
   Did you go to the movies? Which cinema did you go to?
   Did you go to a museum? Which museum did you go to?
   Did you go out dancing? Where did you go dancing?

2. Write down the names of all the places mentioned in the interview.

3. Both students review the list at the end of the interview and make sure all place names are capitalized correctly.

4. Then switch roles and conduct a second interview with your partner.

5. Each student will write a letter to the other, using the list generated in the interview, about places of interest he or she has visited recently.

6. Partners exchange and read letters. Check for any errors in capitalization in each other's letters.

> **To simplify the game:** Have an English-proficient person conduct the interview and write down the place names.
>
> **To increase the challenge:** Write a letter to a friend or family member, telling them about some places of interest you have visited recently. Write and address an envelope. Check letter and envelope for correct use of capitalization. Mail the letter.

▷ REAL-LIFE LANGUAGE

A. PREPARE DINNER

Jonathan and Liam are preparing dinner. Read the narrative that follows, paying special attention to the use of end marks and commas. Punctuation appears in boldface type.

Jonathan and Liam are preparing dinner**.**

"What are we going to make___**(1)**___" asked Liam.

"Grenadier Mash," said Jonathan.

"What's that?" asked Liam.

"It's an old recipe from my mother's family. It's really good ___**(2)**___"Jonathan exclaimed.

"How do we make it?" Liam wanted to know.

"First, we wash___**(3)**___ peel___**(3)**___ and cut the carrots and the broccoli."

"I'm finished with the broccoli," said Liam. "What do I do next?"

"Get the potatoes out of the refrigerator. Peel them, wash them, cut them into cubes, and put them in a pot of water on the stove." Liam added, "Don't forget to put some salt in the water."

"I can't wait for this to be ready," said Liam, peeling the potatoes. "I'm already hungry___**(4)**___"

"Be patient! As my mother always says, this isn't a fast food restaurant!"

"Why is this dish called Grenadier Mash?" asked Liam.

"According to my grandmother, a Grenadier was a rank of soldier. Grenadier Mash was just a simple dish that could feed a lot of people. You know, soldiers have big appetites!"

"Well, I may not be a soldier, but I think I could eat a horse right now!"

"Hang on! If we prepare everything correctly, dinner will be ready in half an hour."

REAL-LIFE LANGUAGE

B. LANGUAGE SKILLS

The following sentences are from the reading passage above. Write the letter of the answer that correctly punctuates each sentence.

____ **1.** What are we going to make
    A period
    B question mark
    C exclamation point

____ **2.** It's really good
    A period
    B question mark
    C exclamation point

____ **3.** First we wash█ peel█ and cut the carrots and the broccoli.
    A period
    B comma
    C colon

____ **4.** I'm already hungry
    A period
    B question mark
    C exclamation point

C. LANGUAGE SKILLS

Write the letter for the punctuation that correctly completes each sentence.

BASIC

____ **1.** Last night I had an incredible dream
    A period
    B comma
    C question mark
    D exclamation point

____ **2.** I was on a boat and it was rapidly sinking
    A period
    B comma
    C question mark
    D exclamation point

____ **3.** What do you think I did
    A period
    B comma
    C question mark
    D exclamation point

INTERMEDIATE

____ **4.** To my surprise█ I suddenly found I had wings!
    A period
    B comma
    C question mark
    D exclamation point

____ **5.** I thought I was saved; I was█ however█ quite wrong.
    A period
    B comma
    C question mark
    D exclamation point

____ **6.** I found myself flying through a storm of swirling papers█ notebooks█ index cards█ and pens.
    A period
    B comma
    C question mark
    D exclamation point

ADVANCED

____ **7.** That█ if you want to know the truth█ was the worst nightmare I have ever had.
    A period
    B comma
    C question mark
    D exclamation point

____ **8.** I kept looking for land█ but it never appeared.
    A period
    B comma
    C question mark
    D exclamation point

____ **9.** When I woke up in the morning, I found I had fallen asleep with an open book on my head█
    A period
    B comma
    C question mark
    D exclamation point

LANGUAGE

A DIFFERENT APPROACH

READING A RECIPE　　TACTILE GRAMMAR

Materials

several recipes cut from the food pages of your local newspaper
dictionary

1. With a partner, choose a recipe from a newspaper.

2. Read the recipe over once to make sure you understand all the words. Look up any words you do not know.

3. Read the recipe over again aloud, slowly.

4. Examine each sentence. Discuss the punctuation and end marks.

5. Read the recipe aloud again, emphasizing the pauses and the ending, indicated by punctuation.

> **To simplify the game:** Have an English-proficient person help identify and look up unknown words, and assist in the reading.
>
> **To increase the challenge:** One student reads the recipe aloud, and the other person student indicates where the punctuation goes.

CREATE A COOKBOOK　　ORAL GRAMMAR

Working with partners, follow these steps to help you write down your favorite recipe.

1. Ask your partner questions about how to make his or her favorite recipe.
What is your favorite recipe?
What are the ingredients you need?
What do you do first?
What do you do next?

2. Write the name of the recipe. List the ingredients. Write down the steps needed to prepare this dish.

3. Discuss the use of punctuation in each sentence. Decide what punctuation is called for and where it should go.

4. Switch roles so that each partner generates a recipe.

5. When everyone is finished writing, each student reads his/her recipe aloud, slowly, pausing to accentuate the use of punctuation.

6. Make any necessary corrections.

> **To simplify the exercise:** Have an English-proficient volunteer review each recipe and help make corrections to punctuation.
>
> **To increase the challenge:** Students work alone to write down their recipes.

LANGUAGE

CHAPTER 16 ITALICS AND QUOTATION MARKS

▷ REAL-LIFE LANGUAGE

A. HOMEWORK OR REPORT

Angelica, Jeremy, and Jaclyn are working on an essay for their English class. Read the narrative that follows, paying special attention to the use of italics and quotation marks.

Angelica, Jeremy, and Jaclyn were working together at the library on a homework assignment. They had to write an essay in response to the quotation: "Love is a many splendored thing." They were supposed to refer to books or plays, movies, and poetry that they had read or seen this semester.

"What does this word __(1)__?" asked Angelica.

"Let's look it up in the dictionary," suggested Jeremy.

In the dictionary they found the words *splendor* and *splendid*, which meant something to do with beauty or brilliance.

They had just read __(2)__ in their English class.

"Remember when Romeo compares Juliet to the sun?" Jacyln remembered. "He says, 'What light in yonder window breaks? 'tis the East, and Juliet is the sun.' She was the sun for him," Jaclyn added.

They recalled that they had also seen the movie, "West Side Story."

"It's the same love story, only set in modern times," said Jeremy.

"I love that beautiful song, 'Maria,' that the hero sings," said Angelica.

"There was also that funny song," Jaclyn added, "called 'I like to live in America.'"

Jeremy said __(3)__. "That song isn't __(4)__," he pointed out.

"*Amor* means 'love' in Spanish," Angelica explained.

"We have a play and a movie. We still need to find a love poem," Jaclyn sighed.

"I've got it!" said Jeremy. "Remember the poem we read by Elizabeth Barrett Browning? 'How do I love thee? Let me count the ways.'"

"That's it!" agreed Angelica.

"Let's get out those books so we can refer to them," said Jaclyn.

Soon they were all at work writing their papers.

B. LANGUAGE SKILLS

The following sentences are from the reading passage above. Choose the letter that shows the correct use of underlining, italics, or quotation marks.

____ **1.** "What does this word ■?" asked Angelica.
   A splendored *mean*
   B *splendored* mean
   C splendored mean

____ **2.** They had just read ■ in their English class.
   A <u>Romeo and Juliet</u> by Shakespeare
   B <u>Romeo and Juliet by Shakespeare</u>
   C <u>Romeo</u> and <u>Juliet</u> by Shakespeare

____ **3.** Jeremy said ■.
   A "that they were getting off the subject."
   B that "they were getting off the subject."
   C that they were getting off the subject.

____ **4.** "That song isn't ■," he pointed out.
   A about amor
   B *about amor*
   C about *amor*

C. LANGUAGE SKILLS

Write the letter of the sentence that is correctly punctuated.

BASIC

____ **1. A** Have you started yet? "Maya asked."
   B "Have you started yet?" Maya asked.
   C "Have you started yet,"? Maya asked.

____ **2. A** "I sure did, Maya groaned, and the math is impossible!"
   B "I sure did, Maya groaned," and the math is impossible!
   C "I sure did," Maya groaned, "and the math is impossible!"

INTERMEDIATE

____ **3. A** Alice said that she would bring her book over to Maya's table.
   B Alice said that "she would bring her book over to Maya's table."
   C Alice "said that she would bring her book over to Maya's table."

____ **4. A** "I guess 'Don't Worry, Be Happy' is her theme song," Alice remarked.
   B "I guess Don't Worry, Be Happy is her theme song," Alice remarked.
   C I guess "Don't Worry, Be Happy" is her theme song, Alice remarked.

ADVANCED

____ **5. A** Have you ever read the novel, <u>A Tale of Two Cities</u>?
   B Have you ever read the novel, <u>A Tale of Two Cities</u>?
   C Have you ever read the novel, <u>A Tale of Two Cities</u>,?

____ **8. A** My favorite story is An "Occurrence" at Owl Creek Bridge.
   B My favorite story is An Occurrence at "Owl Creek Bridge."
   C My favorite story is "An Occurrence at Owl Creek Bridge."

A DIFFERENT APPROACH

WRITING A FOREIGN PHRASE IN A SENTENCE   TACTILE GRAMMAR

Materials

   paper and pencils

Write two sentences that explain or use two different words or phrases from your language of origin in an English sentence.

1. Write sentences on the board and/or read them aloud to the class.

2. Ask classmates to indicate where the italics should go.

> **To simplify the game:** Dictate sentences to an English-proficient student.
>
> **To increase the challenge:** Add the correct punctuation to your own sentences.

WRITE A DIALOGUE   ORAL GRAMMAR

Pairs of students work together to write a four-line dialogue.

1. Work with a partner to write a four-line dialogue between two friends meeting in the hallway.

2. Proofread sentences to make sure that quotation marks are properly used.

3. Read dialogues aloud to the class.

> **To simplify the game:** Have an English-proficient student proofread the dialogue.
>
> **To increase the challenge:** Write a dialogue that uses italics for a title, italics with a word or letter used to represent itself, and italics with a foreign word.

▷ REAL-LIFE LANGUAGE

A. SHOPPING

Four girls are going shopping. Read the narrative that follows, paying special attention to the use of apostrophes, semicolons and colons, hyphens, dashes, and parentheses. These types of punctuation appear in boldface.

Samantha, Cho, Kytoya, and Rosalis were going shopping. They were in great spirits: it was the weekend, the school prom was coming up, and they all had dates. Their only problem was—what to wear?

They were all a little nervous___**(1)**___ none had been to a prom. Samantha was going with Cho's brother; Cho was going with her best friend Larry; Kytoya was going with Rosalis' cousin; and Rosalis was going with Manuel. The girls were all determined___**(2)**___if they could manage it___**(2)**___to find their dresses for the prom.

They had heard that Ladybugs was having a sale on prom dresses, so they headed over there. They couldn't have timed it better; the sale was just starting and the racks were full of dresses.

"Who's this one for?" said Cho, holding up a lacy green dress.

"I've always looked good in green," said Samantha, looking the dress over.

"Isn't this one for you, Rosalis?" said Kytoya, holding out a bright red dress with flounces. "You___**(3)**___ll look great in this when you___**(3)**___re dancing with Manuel."

"This one's a real bargain," said Samantha. "It's only $19.99." She was talking about a dark-red dress with a black-velvet trim.

"That's for me!" said Cho.

"I think I've found mine!" announced Kytoya. She held out a pink dress. ___**(4)**___Pink was her favorite color.___**(4)**___

The day's success was celebrated afterwards with everybody's favorite— ice cream sodas at Crazy Jane's.

LANGUAGE

REAL-LIFE LANGUAGE

B. LANGUAGE SKILLS

The following sentences are from the reading passage above. Write the letter of the answer of the correctly punctuated sentence.

____ 1. **A** They were all a little nervous. none had been to a prom.

  B They were all a little nervous, none had been to a prom.

  C They were all a little nervous; none had been to a prom.

____ 2. **A** The girls were all determined: if they could manage it: to find their dresses for the prom.

  B The girls were all determined; if they could manage it; to find their dresses for the prom.

  C The girls were all determined—if they could manage it—to find their dresses for the prom.

____ 3. **A** You,ll look great in this when you,re dancing with Manuel.

  B You'll look great in this when you're dancing with Manuel.

  C You-ll look great in this when you-re dancing with Manuel.

____ 4. **A** She held out a pink dress. (Pink was her favorite color.)

  B She held out a pink dress. —Pink was her favorite color.—

  C She held out a pink dress. "Pink was her favorite color."

C. LANGUAGE SKILLS

Write the letter of the correctly punctuated sentence.

BASIC

____ 1. **A** The shower was held at Alice Jacksons' house.

  B The shower was held at Alice Jacksons's house.

  C The shower was held at Alice Jackson's house.

____ 2. **A** Alice's generosity was truly overwhelming.

  B Alices' generosity was truly overwhelming.

  C Alices's generosity was truly overwhelming.

INTERMEDIATE

____ 3. **A** Alice was maid of—honor at Fransiska and Reynaldos' wedding.

  B Alice was maid, of honor, at Fransiska and Reynaldos's wedding.

  C Alice was maid-of-honor at Fransiska and Reynaldo's wedding.

____ 4. **A** I hope everybodys' pictures come out.

  B I hope everybodys's pictures come out.

  C I hope everybody's pictures come out.

ADVANCED

____ 5. **A** My brother, however, believes it's a boy.

  B My brother, however believes it's a boy.

  C My brother, however— believes it's a boy.

____ 6. **A** My parents are more excited than anyone. this will be their first grandchild.

  B My parents are more excited than anyone, this will be their first grandchild.

  C My parents are more excited than anyone; this will be their first grandchild.

A DIFFERENT APPROACH

....

SHOPPING GAME TACTILE GRAMMAR

Materials

magazines or newspapers with colorful advertisements for clothing

On the board, write out a list of the possessive form of singular nouns such as: *the girl's; the boy's*. Write the possessive form of plural nouns: *the girls', the boys'*. Also make a list of possessive pronouns: *my, mine, your, yours, his, her, hers, its, our, ours, their*, and *theirs*.

1. A volunteer holds up one advertisement, then asks a question about an article of clothing or object in the ad, such as *Whose hat is that?* or, *Whose cell phone is that?*

2. Other students take turns answering the questions with a complete sentence, such as *That hat is hers*, or, *That is the woman's hat. That cell phone is his. That is the man's cell phone.*

3. When a student answers a question correctly, that student then takes the picture and asks the next question of the group.

4. Continue until everyone has both asked and answered a question about possession correctly.

> **To simplify the game:** Have an English-proficient student ask the questions.
>
> **To increase the challenge:** Students answer the question in two ways, first with a possessive noun, and then with a possessive pronoun.

REPORT ON A FASHION SHOW ORAL GRAMMAR

1. Half the students "model" their clothes down a make-shift runway. They can add hats, coats, or just "model" their clothes.

2. The other half of the students takes notes on the styles and clothes.

3. They write up a fashion review, paying particular attention to apostrophes, semicolons and colons, hyphens, dashes, and parentheses.

4. Students switch roles.

> **To simplify the exercise:** Limit the focus of the writing to the use of possessive nouns and pronouns. Have an English-proficient student read each review and help make corrections to punctuation.
>
> **To increase the challenge:** The students switch papers and read over each other's work, checking for the correct use of punctuation.

LANGUAGE

▶ **READING**

Read the passage and answer the questions that follow.

WHAT TO DO
IF YOU SEE A BEAR [1]

If you are hiking or camping where there might be bears, here are some suggestions:

- **Make a lot of noise.** Let bears know you are there, so they can avoid you. Usually, bears will only attack people when someone gets between a mother bear and her cubs, surprises a bear, or gets between a bear and its food.

Black bear

- **Stay where you are, wave your arms, and talk to the bear.** Bears, like all animals, are aware when humans are fearful. [2] Bears know that a frightened being is dangerous and unpredictable. Instead, wave your arms and talk to—rather than shout at—the bear. The bear will usually walk away.

- **Keep a clean camp.** Put your food and garbage in a bag and place it high over a tree branch. Never keep food in your tent or in your car. Hungry bears will sometimes break car doors or windshields.

- **Learn about the area.** Contact local Park Rangers before your hike. Then you will know where the bears might be and feel more prepared.

Seeing a bear in its natural environment is an experience few people have. It is an exciting encounter with nature. However, it is also an experience you should approach with caution. [3]

Grizzly bear

Guided Reading

1. What do you think is the author's attitude, based on the title?

2. Which statement supports the idea that bears understand fear?

3. How does the author conclude the passage?

Determining the meaning of words

____ **1.** Which statement is the best example of approaching bears with *caution*?

   A Usually, bears will only attack people who get between them and their cubs.

   B Bears are aware when humans are fearful.

   C Wave your arms and talk to—rather than shout at—the bear.

   D Contact your local Park Ranger.

[Look for the word *caution*, and think of the words near it that suggest its meaning.]

[Does the attack of a bear indicate caution?]

[Does the awareness of a bear indicate caution?]

[Does this behavior show caution when you are approaching a bear?]

[Does this behavior show caution?]

Summarizing

____ **2.** Which of the following best describes the main idea of "What to Do If You See a Bear"?

   A Bears are dangerous wild animals that should be avoided.

   B Bears like surprises.

   C Keep food in a tree when camping.

   D Learn what to expect from bears before hiking or camping.

[How would you describe this passage to a friend? What would you say?]

[Is the wildness of bears the most important idea?]

[Where do you see this information?]

[Is this the most important idea?]

[Is knowing what to expect the most important idea?]

Making inferences and generalizations

____ **3.** If you put your food in your car, the bear will probably—

   A attack you

   B go away

   C eat your food

   D sense fear

[The key word is *probably*. You are trying to figure out *what is likely to happen*.]

[Where is information about when you can expect a bear to attack?]

[Where is information about when a bear will simply go away?]

[Does this information connect?]

[Does this information connect?]

Identifying supporting ideas

____ **4.** Why does the writer recommend that hikers make a lot of noise?

   A Bears don't like noise.

   B The bears will know you are near, and they will avoid you.

   C Bears prefer a noisy environment; it helps them to relax.

   D Bears don't hear very well; noise helps them to be aware of the presence of others.

[The key words are *why* and *noise*.]

[Where do you see this information?]

[Where do you see this information?]

[Do you see information that suggests that bears prefer a noisy environment?]

[Where do you see information that suggests that bears don't hear well?]

▶ COMPOSITION

Imagine that you have read a newspaper article that describes how a park ranger killed a grizzly bear that had attacked a hiker. The ranger said he killed the bear because it seemed to have attacked the person for no reason. Do you agree with his conclusion? What else could have been done? Write a letter to the National Park Service giving your opinion.

PROCESS GUIDE

1. Freewrite for 5 minutes about whether you support the ranger's action or disagree with it.

2. Generate a list of reasons that support your opinions.

3. Use the following diagram to help organize your thoughts. Write your opinion in the top triangle. Then, write your reasons in the reason boxes. Finally, write a conclusion in the bottom triangle.

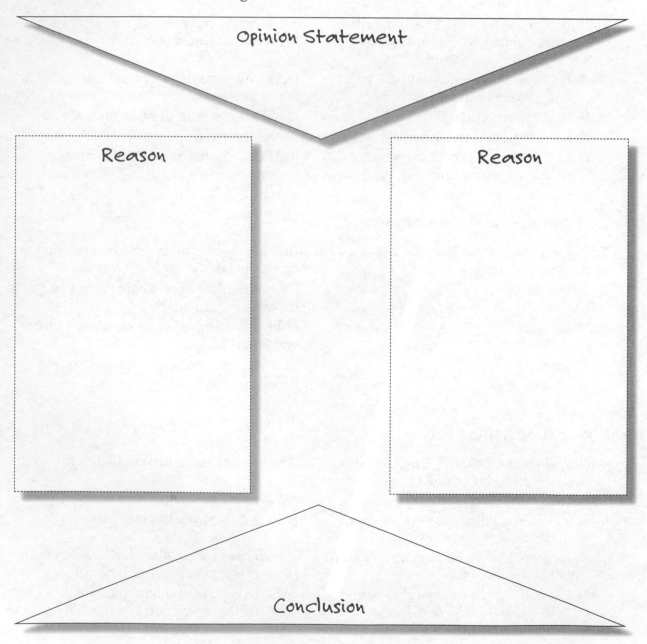

Opinion Statement

Reason

Reason

Conclusion

Read the following passage and determine which type of error, if any, appears in the underlined section. Choose the letter of the correct answer.

Durring the Viking period, many people believed that warriors had the ability
(1)
to become bears or bear-like. They thought that if a warrior put on a bear-skin shirt

(called a bear-sark), which had been treated with oils and herbs then the warrior
(2)
would become as strong and powerful as a bear. While fighting a battle, the warrior,
(3)
would become wild. This is where the word *berserk* comes from. The word *Berserk*
(4)
means "out of control."

____ **1. A** Spelling error   [Are all of the words in this section spelled correctly?]
    B Capitalization error   [Two words are capitalized. Is more or less capitalization needed?]
    C Punctuation error   [There is one comma. Should there be more punctuation?]
    D No error   [Is the spelling, capitalization, and punctuation in this section completely correct?]

____ **2. A** Spelling error   [Are all of the words in this section spelled correctly?]
    B Capitalization error   [Are there words in this section that should be capitalized?]
    C Punctuation error   [There is no punctuation. Should punctuation be added?]
    D No error   [Is the spelling, capitalization, and punctuation in this section completely correct?]

____ **3. A** Spelling error   [Are all of the words in this section spelled correctly?]
    B Capitalization error   [One word is capitalized. Should more words be capitalized?]
    C Punctuation error   [There are two commas and one period in this section. Should there be more or less punctuation?]
    D No error   [Is the spelling, capitalization, and punctuation in this section completely correct?]

____ **4. A** Spelling error   [Are all of the words in this section spelled correctly?]
    B Capitalization error   [Two words are capitalized. Should they both be capitalized?]
    C Punctuation error   [There are quotation marks and a period. Should there be more or less punctuation?]
    D No error   [Is the spelling, capitalization, and punctuation in this section completely correct?]

Read the passage and answer the questions that follow.

SHERMAN ALEXIE'S "THIS IS WHAT IT MEANS TO SAY PHOENIX, ARIZONA"

This is What it Means to Say Phoenix, Arizona is about two young men who take a trip from their Indian Reservation in Washington, to a trailer park in Arizona. Alexie's book is about growing up, being a member of a community, and making peace with the past while learning to move on toward the future. [1]

Victor learns that his father, whom he has not seen in years, has died in Phoenix. Victor doesn't have the money to get to Arizona. He runs into Thomas-Builds-the-Fire, a storyteller, who gives him the money for the trip. Victor and Thomas have known each other their whole lives, yet they are not friends.

Victor's father had been an alcoholic who left his family. Thomas is an orphan who only has his stories for company. Yet the two young men share more in common than they realize. They are both part of the same tribe. They are both trying to learn about how their Native American community fits into America. [2]

Although they are at first almost strangers, the young men begin to care about one another as friends by the end of the book. Because their generosity is unexpected, it is very meaningful to them and to the reader. [3]

Guided Reading

1. What language does the writer use to appeal to the reader's interest?

2. Which details support a reason that the two young men might need one another?

3. How does the author explain why the actions of the young men have meaning?

Sherman Alexie, author

Identifying supporting ideas

____ **1.** Alexie writes about Native Americans in a realistic way—he writes about real, modern problems. Which one statement shows that he does this?

[The key words are *real, modern*, and *problems*. Look for a statement that contains these ideas.]

    A He writes about two boys.

[Does writing about two boys show real, modern problems?]

    B He writes about characters who have bad memories of their past.

[Does writing about bad memories show real, modern problems?]

    C Thomas has an authentic Native American name.

[How is this information connected to problems?]

    D He describes characters who deal with poverty and hopelessness.

[How is information about being poor and hopeless connected to problems?]

Perceiving relationships and recognizing outcomes

____ **2.** Victor agrees to take Thomas with him because—

[The key words are *agrees* and *because*. Reread the passage, and look for why Victor takes Thomas with him.]

    A he feels guilty that he was not kind to Thomas in the past

[Do you see information that suggests that Victor feels guilty?]

    B he wants Thomas to share the driving

[Where do you see information that says this?]

    C Thomas offers to help Victor pay for the trip

[Do you see information that suggests that Thomas has extra money?]

    D Victor is lonely and wants the company

[Where does the passage say that Victor wants company?]

Making inferences and generalizations

____ **3.** After reading the passage, which sentence do you think best describes the theme of *This is What it Means to Say Phoenix, Arizona?*

[The *theme* is the idea *behind* the story. It is not always stated; it is suggested by the story's ideas. It is usually found in the introduction or the conclusion of a passage.]

    A Members of a community are more connected than they realize and need to look out for and help one another.

[Is this an important idea that the writer is trying to express?]

    B Alcoholism is damaging and can ruin relationships.

[This is an important idea. Is it the writer's main idea?]

    C "Cool" people should never socialize with "nerds."

[Do you think that the writer is trying to express this idea?]

    D Native Americans have a hard time living on reservations.

[Where do you see this information?]

▶ COMPOSITION

Sherman Alexie has said that the first time he ever read a collection of Native American literature, he could see his own life in poems and stories. When did you have the experience of recognizing your own life in a work of fiction or poetry? Write two paragraphs describing what it was like.

PROCESS GUIDE

1. Think about how you are like a character in a story you have read, or think of experiences that you have had that are the same as the character's.

2. Limit your examples to those that are most important to you.

3. Use the following word-web diagram to help organize your thoughts.

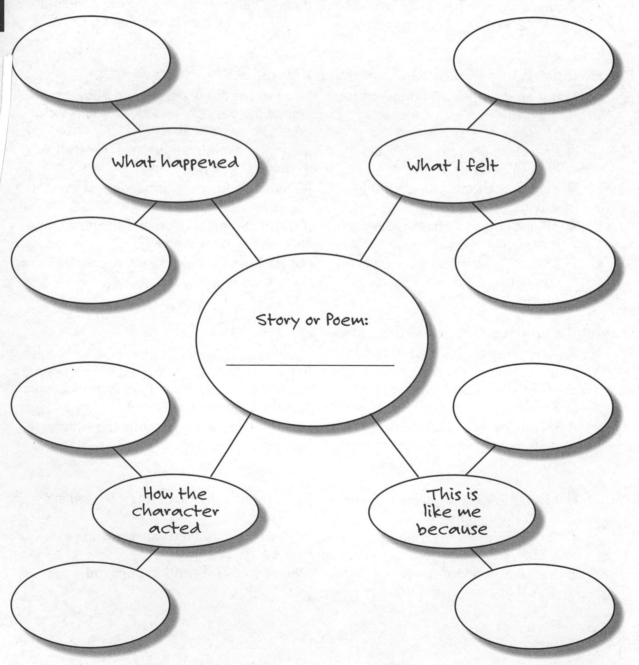

 **EDITING**

Choose the best way to write each underlined section and select the letter for your answer. If the sentence needs no change, circle "Correct as is."

Sherman Alexie planned on being a doctor when he first went to <u>college he</u>
(1)

<u>fainted three times in his anatomy class</u> and decided that he "needed a career

change." Only one course was available. <u>A poetry writing workshop.</u> <u>He made the</u>
(2)   (3)

<u>discovery. To be a writer Since that day,</u> Alexie has published <u>novels, poetry and</u>
(4)

<u>a screenplay.</u>

____ 1. A college. However, he fainted three times in his anatomy class — [Does creating two sentences make two complete thoughts?]

     B college, he fainted three times in his anatomy class — [Does adding a comma create a complete thought?]

     C college and he fainted three times in his anatomy class — [Does adding *and* create a complete thought?]

     D Correct as is — [Is the sentence already a complete thought?]

____ 2. A Only one course was available. The poetry writing workshop. — [Are the two sentences complete thoughts?]

     B Only one course was available, this was being a poetry writing workshop. — [Is this the correct way to create a complete thought?]

     C Only one course, a poetry writing workshop, was available. — [Is this the correct way to create a complete thought?]

     D Correct as is — [Are the sentences already complete thoughts?]

____ 3. A He made the discovery. Realizing he wanted to be a writer. — [Are the two sentences complete thoughts?]

     B He made the discovery, as he realized that he wanted to be a writer. — [Is this the correct way to create a complete thought?]

     C He made the discovery that he wanted to be a writer. — [Is getting rid of the word *he* a way to create a complete thought?]

     D Correct as is — [Are the sentences already complete thoughts?]

____ 4. A Alexie has published novels. Poetry and a screenplay. — [Are the two sentences complete thoughts?]

     B Alexie has published novels— poetry and a screenplay. — [Does the sentence now make more sense?]

     C Alexie has published novels, poetry, screenplay. — [Does getting rid of the words *and a* improve the sentence?]

     D Correct as is — [Is the sentence already a complete thought?]

Read the passage and answer the questions that follow.

WHEN SQUIDS ATTACK

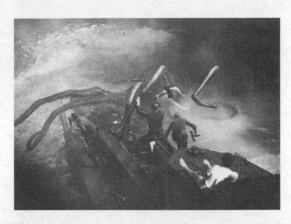

In the 1930s, the *Brunswick*—a 15,000-ton Norwegian ship—was attacked three times by a giant squid. [**1**] The squid would pull up alongside the ship and wrap its tentacles around it. The squid was unable to grip the steel, and it lost its hold on the ship. [**2**]

Giant squids have been known to attack whales, too. In 1965, men on a Soviet whaling boat witnessed a battle between a forty-ton sperm whale and a squid. The whale was later found with the squid's tentacles wrapped around it.

Although some experts argue that the giant squid attacks for food, others say that the squid is trying to find a ride. [**3**] Giant squids live in cold water. This cold water can get trapped above a layer of warm water, pushing the squid to the surface. This may explain why we see giant squid in areas where cold and warm water meet. The squid's ability to float makes it difficult for it to sink beneath the warm water, back to the cold water where it needs to go. Some scientists suggest that a squid attaches itself to a whale because whales dive deeply into the water. Boats may look like whales to giant squids, which may explain the *Brunswick* attack.

Guided Reading

1. How does the writer get your attention in the first sentence?

2. What is the main idea in this paragraph?

3. Which details support the argument that squids attack in order to get back to the cold water they live in?

Submersibles aid in underwater studies

Determining the meaning of words

____ **1.** Which word or words could be substituted for the word *witnessed* in the second paragraph, without changing the meaning of the sentence?

[Look for the words around *witnessed* that give you clues as to the action that is taking place.]

   A participated in   [Did the whalers take part in the battle?]
   B proved   [What was proved during the battle?]
   C excited   [Did something get excited in the battle?]
   D watched   [Did the whalers watch the battle?]

Summarizing

____ **2.** Some experts feel that giant squids attack boats because—

[Look for reasons that show why squids attack boats.]

   A they don't see well   [Where is information about eyesight?]
   B they think the boats are whales   [Where is this information?]
   C they are protecting their young   [Where is information about baby squids?]
   D they hunt and eat humans   [Is there information that suggests that squids attack humans?]

Perceiving relationships and recognizing outcomes

____ **3.** When warm water in the ocean combines with cold water—

[Look for information that will help you finish this sentence. The key word is *combines*.]

   A the water becomes too warm for the giant squid to live in   [Where do you see this information?]
   B cold water may get trapped above warm water   [Do you see information that shows that water gets trapped?]
   C Giant squids will go searching for food   [Where is information that connects their food search to water?]
   D Giant squids will enjoy the warmer water   [Do you see information that shows that squids enjoy warm water?]

Recognizing points of view

____ **4.** The purpose of this passage can best be described as—

[The key word is *purpose*. Think about *why* the author may have wanted to write this passage.]

   A To explain why giant squids are dangerous to whales   [Does the writer emphasize the danger to whales?]
   B To give information about giant squids   [Is the writer trying to inform, or educate, the reader?]
   C To persuade people to support giant squid research   [Where do you see the writer trying to convince the reader to support research?]
   D To frighten people and make them aware that giant squids are dangerous   [Do you find this passage frightening? Do you think that the writer is trying to warn the reader?]

TEST PREPARATION • UNIT 3

▷ COMPOSITION

Write a few informative paragraphs about the roles that mythical creatures play in our society.

PROCESS GUIDE

1. Freewrite for 5 minutes about some mythical creatures with which you are familiar.

2. Generate a list of reasons you think these creatures are important.

3. Use the following organizer to help you collect your ideas.

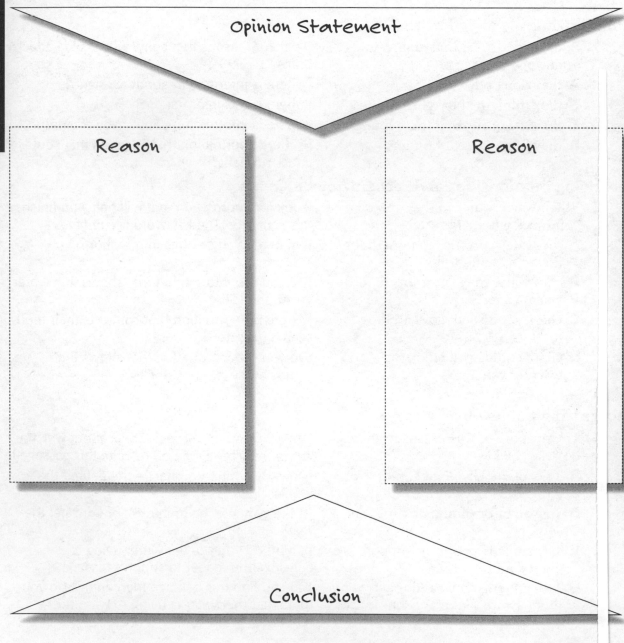

Opinion Statement

Reason

Reason

Conclusion

▶ EDITING

Read the following passage and determine which word or group of words belongs in each space. Select the letter of the correct answer.

The ship sailed silently in the night. A cool breeze **(1)** the clouds,

showing the full moon hanging in the sky. The night was still and calm, and the

ocean itself seemed to be asleep.

Suddenly, the ship **(2)** unsteadily. The night watchman awakened from

his nap. Rubbing **(3)** eyes in disbelief, he watched as a giant tentacle wrapped

itself around the ship's bow. "Captain!" he yelled. The word barely **(4)** out of

his throat. "Captain! Come quickly!"

_____ **1. A** stirred   [The verb *stirred* is in the past tense. Does this tense fit the story?]
　　　 B did stirred   [Is this the correct form of the verb?]
　　　 C is stirring   [The verb *is stirring* is in the present tense. Does this tense fit the story?]
　　　 D will stir   [The verb *will stir* is in the future tense. Does this tense fit the story?]

_____ **2. A** did rocked   [Is this the correct form of the verb?]
　　　 B rocked   [The verb *rocked* is in the past tense. Does this tense fit the story?]
　　　 C is rocking   [The verb *is rocking* is in the present tense. Does this tense fit the story?]
　　　 D were rocking   [The verb *were rocking* is plural and in the past tense. Does this tense fit the story?]

_____ **3. A** her   [The word *her* is singular and feminine. Does it go with the subject?]
　　　 B his   [The word *his* is singular and masculine. Does it go with the subject?]
　　　 C their   [The word *their* is plural. Does it go with the subject?]
　　　 D our   [The word *our* is plural. Does it go with the subject?]

_____ **4. A** are squeaking   [The verb *are squeaking* is plural and in the present tense. Does this tense fit the story?]
　　　 B squeak   [The verb *squeak* is plural and in the present tense. Does this tense fit the story?]
　　　 C squeaks   [The verb *squeaks* is singular and in the present tense. Does this tense fit the story?]
　　　 D squeaked   [The verb *squeaked* is in the past tense. Does this tense fit the story?]

TEST PREPARATION • UNIT 3

READING

Read the passage and answer the questions that follow.

YOU CALL THIS A VACATION? [1]

When I was thirteen years old, my parents rented a home for the summer. My sisters and I discovered that it was just a cabin—and not even a nice cabin. It was an old wreck. There was no television. There wasn't even a radio. [2] What were we supposed to do for two weeks? We begged our parents to take us back home.

However, after about three days, we found things to do. We played games and told stories. One night when our parents were out, we wrote a play. When our parents returned, the cabin was transformed into a theater.

Even more important, I started to enjoy reading and nature. I became caught up in the imaginative world of my books, and I began to appreciate the mountains that surrounded us. They were so high they still had snowy peaks, even in the middle of summer. I was no longer bored.

Although we would never have admitted it to our parents, that trip was one of the best that we have ever had. We learned to enjoy each other's company and work together. Instead of arguing the way we always did, we had fun. [3]

Guided Reading

1. How does the writer show his or her attitude in the title?

2. Which information gives you a clue about the main idea of the passage?

3. Were you surprised by the writer's conclusion? Why or why not?

Determining the meaning of words

____ **1.** In the second paragraph, which word could be substituted for *transformed* without changing the meaning of the sentence?
    A moved
    B enjoyed
    C changed
    D removed

[Reread the second paragraph. Look at the word *transformed*. What happened to the cabin?]

[Did the cabin move?]
[Did the cabin enjoy something?]
[Did the cabin change?]
[Was the cabin removed?]

Identifying supporting ideas

____ **2.** Which one of the following did the sisters NOT do on their trip?

    A create a play
    B complain about how there was nothing to do
    C learn how to climb rocks
    D play games together

[The key word is *not*. Look for information that shows you what they did, and see whether it matches any of the phrases below.]
[Did the sisters create a play?]
[Did they complain?]

[Did they go hiking?]
[Did they play games?]

Summarizing

____ **3.** What is the main idea of the first paragraph?
    A The cabin was run-down, and the children were disappointed.
    B My parents agreed with us.
    C Learning to amuse oneself is a valuable skill.
    D There were plenty of activities for the children.

[Reread the first paragraph. How would you describe the main idea to someone else?]
[Is this the most important idea?]

[Where do you see this information?]
[Is this the most important idea in the first paragraph?]
[Where do you see this information?]

Recognizing statements of opinion

____ **4.** Based on the passage, the writer's reaction to this vacation may be *best* described as—
    A upset
    B angry
    C surprised

    D foolish

[This kind of information should be in the conclusion, because it refers to the writer's general opinion of his or her vacation.]
[In general, does the writer seem unhappy?]
[In general, does the writer seem annoyed?]
[Was the experience different from what the writer expected?]
[Does the writer seem silly to you?]

TEST PREPARATION • UNIT 4

What difficult experience have you had that you can describe? What did you learn from the experience? Write two paragraphs that describe your experience.

PROCESS GUIDE

1. If you wish, you can describe your experience in a funny way. Make it interesting for the reader. You might want to include people who did (or did not) help you.

2. Choose one part of your experience to describe in detail. Explain what the experience was, why it was difficult, how you faced it and how you feel about it.

3. Use the word web below to help you organize your thoughts.

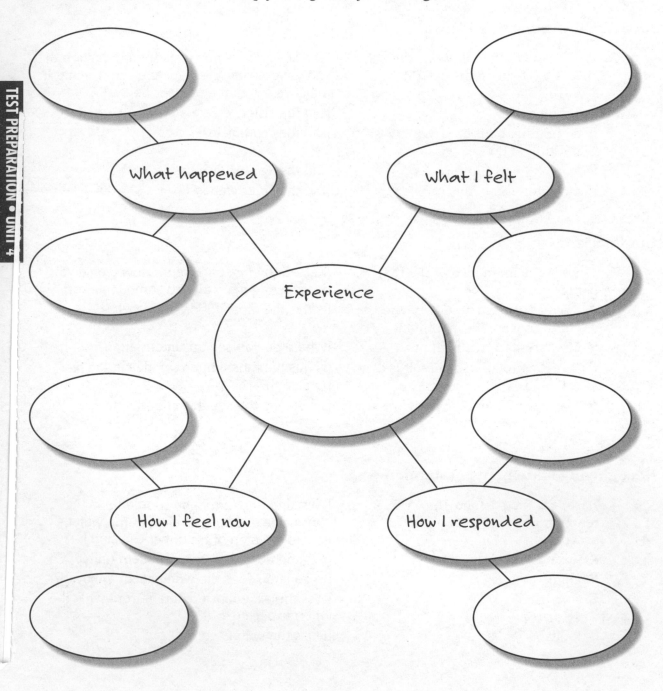

▶ EDITING

Read the following passage and determine which type of error, if any, appears in the underlined section. Select the letter of the correct answer.

Dear Sarah,

Last week was the worst week I've spent in my whole life. Debbie and I had

nothing to do, <u>so we had a misquito bite contest.</u> I won because I had twenty-five
(1)

bites. I can't wait to leave this cabin and these mountains. <u>Theres nothing to do and</u>
(2)

<u>I miss my friends.</u> <u>I can't believe, I have to spend two entire weeks here.</u> <u>I hate</u>
(3)   (4)

whoever suggested this place!

I have never been so miserable.

Sadly yours,

Jessica

____ **1. A** Spelling error   [Are all of the words in the section spelled correctly?]
       B Capitalization error [Should any of the words be capitalized?]
       C Punctuation error [There is one period. Should there be more punctuation?]
       D No error [Is every part of the section correct, with no spelling, capitalization, or punctuation errors?]

____ **2. A** Spelling error   [Are all of the words in the section spelled correctly?]
       B Capitalization error [One word is capitalized. Should more words be capitalized?]
       C Punctuation error [There is one period. Should there be more punctuation?]
       D No error [Is every part of the section correct, with no spelling, capitalization, or punctuation errors?]

____ **3. A** Spelling error   [Are all of the words in the section spelled correctly?]
       B Capitalization error [One word is capitalized. Should more words be capitalized?]
       C Punctuation error [There is one comma and one period. Should there be more or less punctuation?]
       D No error [Is every part of the section correct, with no spelling, capitalization, or punctuation errors?]

____ **4. A** Spelling error   [Are all of the words in the section spelled correctly?]
       B Capitalization error [One word is capitalized. Should more words be capitalized?]
       C Punctuation error [There is one exclamation point. Should there be more or less punctuation?]
       D No error [Is every part of the section correct, with no spelling, capitalization, or punctuation errors?]

Read the passages and answer the questions that follow.

FORTITUDINE VINCIMUS—
BY ENDURANCE WE CONQUER

Ernest Shackleton discovered the truth of his family's motto *Fortitudine Vincimus* ("By endurance we conquer"), after he set out on his expedition to the Antarctic in August of 1914. [1] First, his ship, the *Endurance* became trapped in ice and remained stuck for ten months. Finally, the men abandoned their ship and camped on drifting pieces of ice for five months. When the ice disintegrated, they used their lifeboats. On April 12, 1916, Shackleton and his crew landed on Elephant Island—their first steps on land in sixteen months.

While landing on Elephant Island was a great triumph, it didn't get the men out of trouble. The nearest food and shelter was 800 miles northwest of them, on South Georgia Island.

Sixteen days later, Shackleton and his crew landed safely on South Georgia Island. However, they were seventeen mountainous miles from the whaling station they were trying to reach. Yet Shackleton and his men had to cross an icy mountain range—thought to be impossible to successfully pass—if they were to survive.

Miraculously, every man survived the difficult journey of the *Endurance*. [2] They survived as a result of their strength, and they survived because they believed in themselves and in their goal. [3]

Guided Reading

1. How does the use of the word endurance, which means "strength," add to the meaning of the writer's description?

2. Find a detail that supports how difficult the journey was.

3. How does the writer conclude the passage?

The *Endurance*.

The *Endurance* was crushed by ice.

Determining the meaning of words

____ **1.** What is the meaning of the word *abandoned*, as used in this passage?

    A boarded
    B explored
    C bandaged
    D left

[Find the word *abandoned*, and look for the words and sentences that surround it. What clues do they give you about its meaning?]
[Did the men go on the ship?]
[Did the men look around on the ship?]
[Did the men wrap the ship?]
[Did the men go off the ship?]

Summarizing

____ **2.** Which sentence best reflects the main idea of the first paragraph?

    A The *Endurance* became trapped in ice and had to be abandoned.
    B Shackleton bravely led his men to safety.
    C Giant waves hit Shackleton and his crew.
    D Shackleton's crew worried when the *Endurance* was crushed by ice.

[Reread the first paragraph. How can you sum up the important information?]
[Do you see this information? Is it the most important idea?]
[Where do you see this information?]

[Where is this information in the paragraph?]

[Where is information that suggests that the men lost hope early in their journey?]

Making inferences and generalizations

____ **3.** Based on the passage, Shackleton's journey can best be described as—

    A a heroic effort under difficult circumstances
    B a humorous adventure
    C a frightening lesson

    D an amazing education about sea life

[The key words are *best* and *described*. Imagine yourself describing the journey. Which kind of adjectives would you use?]
[Would you consider Shackleton and his men to be brave?]
[Was the passage funny to you?]
[Do you think Shackleton and his men felt that they had done something they shouldn't have?]
[Did the passage describe the creatures of the ocean?]

Recognizing points of view

____ **4.** The tone of this passage can be described as—

    A humorous
    B bitter
    C disorganized
    D suspenseful

[Think about the author's purpose and about how his or her approach—or *tone*—helped this purpose.]
[Did the author wish to be funny?]
[Did the passage seem angry to you?]
[Did the passage make sense?]
[Did the passage create a feeling of tension?]

▶ COMPOSITION

Shackleton wrote about his journey: "We had suffered, starved and triumphed, groveled down yet grasped at glory . . ."

What do you think of Shackleton's summary? Is it necessary to risk death in order to "grasp at glory"? Why do you think humans have been fascinated with exploring new territories through the ages? Write two paragraphs that give your opinion on this subject.

PROCESS GUIDE

1. Think about the human need to explore. Does it make sense to you?

2. Think of a few reasons that explain why humans should or should not explore new places. For each reason, give one detail or example that supports it.

3. Use the chart below to help you organize your thoughts.

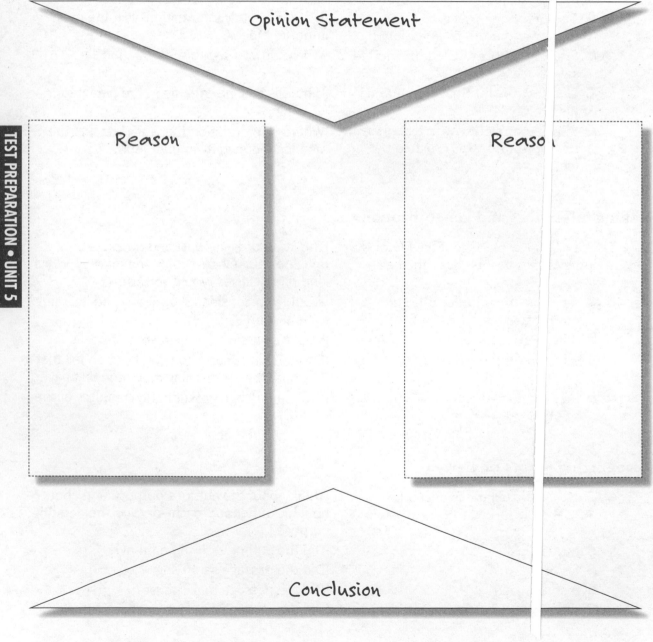

Opinion Statement

Reason

Reason

Conclusion

▶ EDITING

....

Read the following passage and determine which type of error, if any, appears in the underlined section. Select the letter of the correct answer.

<u>another problem Shackleton and his crew faced while camping on the ice was</u>
(1)

<u>killer whales.</u> Spotting a seal, <u>the wails would dive deep down under the sea and</u>
(2)

<u>then smash up through the ice,</u> seizing the seal in its mouth. <u>Shackleton and his</u>
(3)

<u>men found a whole twenty-five feet wide</u> that had been created by a killer whale.

Photographer Frank Hurley, hearing the whales beneath him as he crossed the ice

with his team of dogs, described <u>what he felt; "Never in my life have I looked upon</u>
(4)

more loathsome creatures."

_____ **1. A** Spelling error   [Are all of the words in this section spelled correctly?]
     B Capitalization error   [One word is capitalized. Should there be more or less capitalization?]
     C Punctuation error   [There is one period. Should there be more punctuation?]
     D No error   [Is the entire section correct, with no errors in spelling, capitalization, or punctuation?]

_____ **2. A** Spelling error   [Are all of the words in this section spelled correctly?]
     B Capitalization error   [Should there be any capitalization?]
     C Punctuation error   [There is one comma. Should there be more punctuation?]
     D No error   [Is the entire section correct, with no errors in spelling, capitalization, or punctuation?]

_____ **3. A** Spelling error   [Are all of the words in this section spelled correctly?]
     B Capitalization error   [One word is capitalized. Should there be more or less capitalization?]
     C Punctuation error   [Should there be more punctuation?]
     D No error   [Is the entire section correct, with no errors in spelling, capitalization, or punctuation?]

_____ **4. A** Spelling error   [Are all of the words in this section spelled correctly?]
     B Capitalization error   [Should there be any capitalization?]
     C Punctuation error   [There is one semicolon. Is this the right punctuation?]
     D No error   [Is the entire section correct, with no errors in spelling, capitalization, or punctuation?]

TEST PREPARATION • UNIT 5

Read the passages and answer the questions that follow.

SPORTS HEROES DESERVE HIGH SALARIES

Sports heroes are paid just what we consumers think they deserve. If team owners are going to make hundreds of millions of dollars from their team, why shouldn't the players benefit also? [1]

Team owners are making more money than ever. In 1986, the Cleveland Indians baseball team was purchased for $45 million. Thirteen years later, the team was sold for $320 million. That same year, the Washington Redskins football team was purchased for $800 million.

It's the athletes' effort and skill that brings in the crowds. Isn't it only fair they should receive a fair share of the profits? [2]

WHAT'S UP WITH SPORTS SALARIES? [3]

One of the biggest mysteries has got to be the salaries paid to professional athletes. According to statistics, from 1950 to 1998, the average American worker's salary rose from roughly $2,800 to $38,800. The average professional baseball player's salary, however, rose from approximately $13,000 in 1950 to $1.4 million in 1998.

What do the high salaries mean, in a world where children go hungry and schools have a lack of funds? What do these high salaries show about our values?

I wonder about athletic skills being more highly valued than educating our youth. A basketball star can make millions of dollars in one season. A high school teacher might earn $35,000.

Michael Jordan is a world famous basketball player

Guided Reading

1. How does the writer get your attention?

2. How does the writer repeat his or her main point in the conclusion?

3. How does the title of the second passage show you the writer's attitude towards his or her subject?

Recognizing statements of opinion

____ **1.** The author of the first article feels that sports stars—

   A are paid too much, because their high salaries raise the ticket prices.

   B should be paid a lot of money, because the owners are making a lot of money.

   C should be better role models.

   D should be paid high salaries, because sports are hard on athlete's bodies.

[The key word is *feels*. This word shows that an opinion is being given. Find an opinion in the first article.]

[Is there information that connects salaries to ticket prices?]

[Is there information that connects salaries to the money made by the owners?]

[Where do you see this information?]

[Where do you see this information?]

Summarizing

____ **2.** According to the second article—

   A high salaries for athletes show that our American values may be in trouble

   B high salaries for athletes show that the team's management is making money

   C players earn their high salaries when they win games

   D being an athlete is more important than being a teacher

[You are looking for a main idea, or a summary.]

[Is this the main idea of the second article?]

[Are these two ideas connected?]

[Do you see this information in the second article?]

[How does the writer connect athletes and teachers?]

Recognizing points of view

____ **3.** The tone of the two passages can best be described as—

   A informal and relaxed

   B formal, like the style of a research paper

   C serious, like the style used for a newspaper article

   D persuasive, like the style used for a political speech

[The key word is *tone*. How does the writer approach his or her subject?]

[Is the writer's language easy to read?]

[Does the writer's language sound like a school paper?]

[Does the writer's language sound like a news report?]

[Does the writer sound like a politician?]

Making inferences and generalizations

____ **4.** The purpose of these articles is to—

   A be angry about the high cost of tickets to sporting events.

   B give opinions about how much money athletes are paid.

   C convince people to stop attending expensive sporting events.

   D explain to people why athletes' salaries are high.

[What is the writer trying to accomplish?]

[Does the writer seem angry about how much tickets cost?]

[Would you say that the writer is mainly trying to express his or her opinion?]

[Do you see this information in the passages?]

[Is the writer mainly trying to inform the reader?]

TEST PREPARATION • UNIT 6

▷ COMPOSITION

Imagine that you own a professional sports team in a small city. You want the best team possible, but you don't have the same money for salaries as teams in larger cities. Write two paragraphs that describe how you feel about this situation.

PROCESS GUIDE

1. Think about whether you believe that this situation is fair. Is there anything you can do to change it?

2. As you express your opinion, limit yourself to reasons that are supported by a few good examples.

3. Use the following chart to help you organize your ideas. Write your opinion statement. Then, give two reasons for your opinion. Finally, write a strong conclusion.

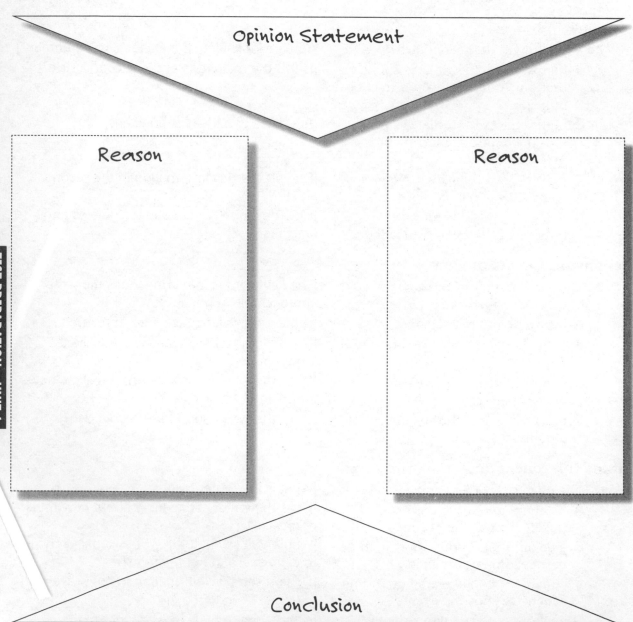

Opinion Statement

Reason

Reason

Conclusion

▶ EDITING

Read the following passage and decide which word or group of words belongs in each space. Select the letter of the correct answer.

My brother and I went to the **_(1)_** basketball game I've ever seen. Our father and a group of his friends played in it. The game was a benefit to raise money for the sports program at our school. The **_(2)_** thing about it was that it was played with donkeys. The court was covered with a special surface, and all the players came out seated on top of the animals. Being seated on top of a donkey sure **_(3)_** my father's game! I think donkeys are even **_(4)_** than my brother or me.

____ **1. A** most excitingest   [Is this the correct form of the adjective?]

     B most exciting   [The adjective *most exciting* means that something is being compared to all other things. Is this the correct form?]

     C more exciting   [The adjective *more exciting* means that something is being compared to one other thing. Is this the correct form?]

     D most excitinger   [Is this the correct form of the adjective?]

____ **2. A** incredible   [The adjective *incredible* describes a noun. Is this the correct form?]

     B incrediblest   [Is this the correct form of the adjective?]

     C most incrediblest   [Is this the correct form of the adjective?]

     D more incredible   [The adjective *more incredible* means that something is being compared to one other thing. Is this the correct form?]

____ **3. A** did improved   [Is this the correct form of the verb?]

     B improves   [The word *improves* is in the present tense. Is this the correct form of the verb?]

     C will improve   [The words *will improve* are in the future tense. Is this the correct form of the verb?]

     D improved   [The word *improved* is in the past tense. Is this the correct form of the verb?]

____ **4. A** most stubbornest   [Is this the correct form of the adjective?]

     B more stubbornest   [Is this the correct form of the adjective?]

     C most stubborn   [The adjective *most stubborn* means that something is being compared to all other things. Is this the correct form?]

     D more stubborn   [The adjective *more stubborn* means that something is being compared to one other thing. Is this the correct form?]

Read the passage and answer the questions that follow.

NEW YORK, NEW YORK

When I was sixteen, I went to New York City with my best friend. I was so excited! I imagined bright lights, Broadway shows, and marvelous museums. [1]

My parents would only let me go if I could earn the money for my airfare from San Diego to New York. So, I got a job. I worked until I had the money to pay for my flight.

On the plane, I was a bundle of excitement. I couldn't wait. When we arrived, we went to New Jersey, where my friend's family had relatives. There was snow on the ground—which I had never seen. I had New York pizza for the first time in New Jersey. It was delicious! Then we headed through the Lincoln Tunnel to the great metropolis. [2]

My friend's father took us all to dinner and a Broadway show. We dressed in our nicest dresses and put on our winter coats. However, December in New York is quite different from December in San Diego. We stepped outside. We looked at each other.

"It's cold." She said, "I hate it. I want to go home." And we laughed. [3]

Guided Reading

1. Which detail supports the idea that the writer really wanted to go to New York?

2. What is the main idea of this paragraph?

3. How does the writer conclude the passage?

Summarizing

____ **1.** Which one statement summarizes the second paragraph?

    A I was able to go to New York because I paid for the trip.

    B My parents liked my sister better than me.

    C My parents encouraged me to travel.

    D I wanted to go more than my friend did.

[The key word is *summarizes*. What is the main idea of the paragraph?]
[Is this the main idea of the paragraph?]

[Where is this information?]

[Where is this information?]

[Where is information about how much the writer's friend wanted to go?]

Making inferences and generalizations

____ **2.** Which one of the following did the author NOT do on her trip?

    A eat New York pizza in New Jersey

    B get prepared to go out for dinner and a show

    C ride the subway to Brooklyn

    D see snow

[The key word is *not*. First, you must figure out what the writer did do.]
[Is this information in the passage?]
[Where do you see this information?]

[Where does the writer mention riding the subway?]

[Where does the writer mention seeing snow?]

Recognizing points of view

____ **3.** The *tone* of this passage can best be described as—

    A light

    B upset

    C serious

    D emotional

[What is the feeling of the passage, based on the language used by the writer?]
[Is the tone easygoing, like in a conversation?]
[Does the writer seem sad?]
[Does the writer have a thoughtful attitude, as though his or her subject is very important?]
[Does the writer consider this an extremely important memory?]

Recognizing statements of opinion

____ **4.** Which one of the following is an opinion from the passage?

    A December in New York is not quite what we expected.

    B I had New York pizza for the first time in New Jersey.

    C My friend's father was taking us all to dinner and a Broadway show.

    D We went to New Jersey, where my friend's family had relatives.

[Find sentences that show how the writer feels or thinks about his or her subject.]
[Is this an opinion that shows the writer's thoughts or feelings?]
[Did this actually happen, or is it an opinion?]

[Can this be proved? Is it a fact?]

[Did this actually happen? Is it a fact?]

TEST PREPARATION • UNIT 7

▶ COMPOSITION

Is there a city or country that you have always wanted to visit? Write a two-paragraph essay for your classmates, describing a place you would like to visit.

PROCESS GUIDE

1. Think about what you think the place will look like and why you want to go.

2. Limit yourself to a few examples that show your reasons for wanting to go.

3. Use the word web below to help you organize your ideas.

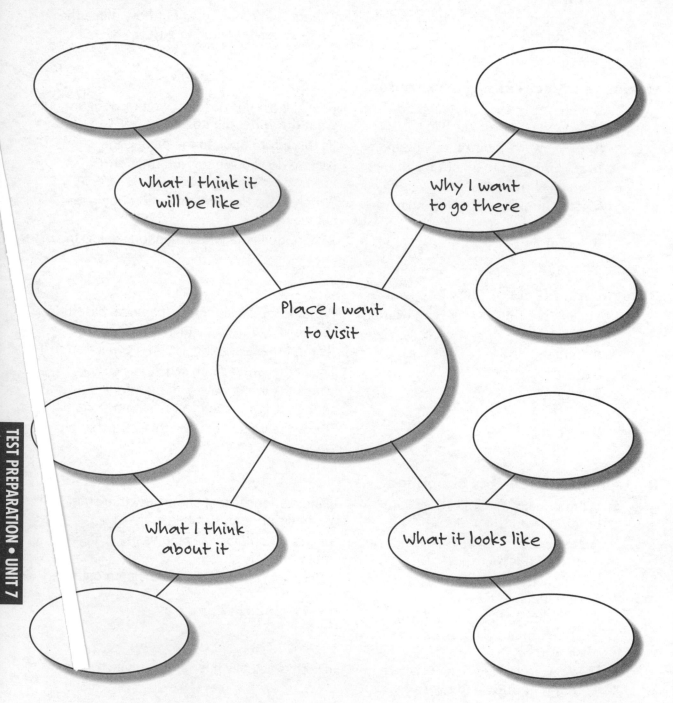

▶ EDITING

Read the following passage and determine which type of error, if any, appears in the underlined section. Circle the letter of the correct answer.

One of my favorite museums in New York City is the Cloisters Museum.

<u>located near the northwestern tip of Manhattan, the museum is filled with art from</u>
                                                (1)

<u>the Middle Ages.</u> Certain parts of the buildings are actually from old structures.

<u>They have things; like tapestries.</u> One of <u>the most gourgeous tapestries shows a</u>
           (2)   **(3)**

unicorn surrounded by flowers. The Cloisters also has an amazing <u>herb garden and</u>
                                                                            (4)

<u>a Wonderful view of the Hudson River.</u>

_____ **1. A** Spelling error   [Are all of the words in the section spelled correctly?]

     B Capitalization error   [There are three capital letters. Is there enough capitalization?]

     C Punctuation error   [There is one comma and one period. Should there be more punctuation?]

     D No error   [Is the section completely correct, with no errors in spelling, punctuation, or capitalization?]

_____ **2. A** Spelling error   [Are all of the words in the section spelled correctly?]

     B Capitalization error   [There is one capital letter. Is there enough capitalization?]

     C Punctuation error   [There is one semicolon and one period. Should there be more or less punctuation?]

     D No error   [Is the section completely correct, with no errors in spelling, punctuation, or capitalization?]

_____ **3. A** Spelling error   [Are all of the words in the section spelled correctly?]

     B Capitalization error   [Should any of these words be capitalized?]

     C Punctuation error   [There is one period. Should there be more punctuation?]

     D No error   [Is the section completely correct, with no errors in spelling, punctuation, or capitalization?]

_____ **4. A** Spelling error   [Are all of the words in the section spelled correctly?]

     B Capitalization error   [There are three capital letters. Is there enough capitalization, or too much?]

     C Punctuation error   [There is one period. Should there be more punctuation?]

     D No error   [Is the section completely correct, with no errors in spelling, punctuation, or capitalization?]

Read the passage and answer the questions that follow.

AN AMERICAN ORIGINAL [1]

Woody Guthrie was an American original. Born in Oklahoma in 1912, he began singing about the working class during the 1930s. Woody was very influenced by the difficulties of others. The Great Depression had taken over America, and twenty-five percent of the population was unemployed. In 1935, drought and dust storms hit farms in Oklahoma, Texas, Arkansas, and much of the Midwest. Woody left home, along with thousands of other out-of-work farmers.

He saw men, woman and children who had lost their belongings, their community, and their jobs. They were trying to build new lives by leaving their homes in search of work in California.

Once they were in California, the problems of these workers became worse than anything they had experienced. [2] Rather than reaching the "Promised Land" that had been advertised to them in flyers, the workers found only wealthy and powerful landowners who would not pay them very much for their hard work.

Woody wrote songs about this experience, which captured the pain of the workers and revealed his understanding of them. Author John Steinbeck wrote that in Woody's songs, "There is the will of the people to endure and fight against oppression. I think we call this the American spirit." [3]

Guided Reading

1. How does the author show his or her attitude towards Woody Guthrie?

2. Which detail supports the idea that the lives of the workers became worse?

3. Why does the writer use this quotation?

Woody Guthrie (singer, songwriter)

Perceiving relationships and recognizing outcomes

____ **1.** What happened in 1935 that made life more difficult for many people? [The key information is *1935*. Look for information that connects to this year.]

  A The Midwest was hit by drought and dust storms. [Does this statement connect to 1935?]

  B There were landowners who hired workers in California. [Did this make life more difficult in 1935?]

  C Guthrie wrote songs about workers. [Did this add to the workers' difficulties in 1935?]

  D Guthrie understood the pain of the workers. [Does this statement connect to 1935?]

Identifying supporting ideas

____ **2.** Woody Guthrie was a supporter of unions—groups that got together to fight for the rights of working people. Which detail suggests a reason for why he supported the unions? [The key words are *why* and *supported*. Look for details that will explain why Guthrie acted as he did.]

  A He saw workers who were being treated unfairly. [Where is this information?]

  B He believed that America was great. [Do you see this information in the passage?]

  C He hoped that the "Promised Land" would give jobs to people. [Does this information connect to the unions?]

  D The Great Depression was hard on people. [How does this information connect to the unions?]

Recognizing points of view

____ **3.** The author probably believes that— [Try to find the point of view of the writer.]

  A Woody Guthrie was a great American writer [Is this a correct statement?]

  B Guthrie should not have been involved in politics [Is this an opinion of the writer?]

  C Guthrie honestly questioned American values [Is this an opinion of the writer?]

  D Guthrie showed weakness by always rambling [Is this a correct statement?]

Determining the meaning of words

____ **4.** Which word could be substituted for *oppression* in the last paragraph, without changing the meaning of the sentence? [Look at the last paragraph, and read the sentence with the word *oppression*. Which words are in or near the sentence that give you clues about its meaning?]

  A government [Did the people fight the government?]

  B cruelty [Were the people trying to deal with cruel behavior on the part of others?]

  C education [Did workers fight education?]

  D work [Did the people fight the idea of working?]

TEST PREPARATION • UNIT 8

▶ COMPOSITION

There are many places in the world today where workers are being treated cruelly,. Write two paragraphs to explain why you think there are not large groups fighting to protect the rights of these workers.

PROCESS GUIDE

1. Think about workers in other countries and some of the problems they might face.

2. Limit yourself to a few reasons that explain why unfair situations have happened.

3. Use the following diagram to help you organize your thoughts.

Situation that is unfair:
Reason #1:
Reason #2:
Conclusion:

EDITING

Read the following passage and determine which word or group of words belongs in each space. Circle the letter of the correct answer.

Woody Guthrie __(1)__ famous for his humor and honest songwriting. He always __(2)__ situations honestly. In the late 1930s, Guthrie sang on a radio station in Los Angeles. When people would call in and ask for the words to his songs, he __(3)__ a small songbook to them. On the bottom of one page, Guthrie __(4)__ permission for people to sing his songs as much as they wanted to.

____ **1. A** did became   [Is this the correct form of the verb?]
    B became   [The word *became* is in the past tense. Is this the correct form?]
    C will become   [The words *will become* are in the future tense. Is this the correct form?]
    D becoming famous   [Is this the correct form of the verb?]

____ **2. A** described   [The verb *described* is in the past tense. Is this the correct form?]
    B describe   [The verb *describe* is in the present tense. Is this the correct form?]
    C will describe   [The words *will describe* are in the future tense. Is this the correct form?]
    D were describing   [The words *were describing* are plural and in the past tense. Is this the correct form?]

____ **3. A** mailed   [The verb *mailed* is in the past tense. Is this the correct form?]
    B mail   [The verb *mail* is in the present tense. Is this the correct form?]
    C were mailing   [The words *were mailing* are plural and in the past tense. Is this the correct form?]
    D will mail   [The words *will mail* are in the future tense. Is this the correct form?]

____ **4. A** gived   [Is this the correct form?]
    B given   [Is this the correct form?]
    C will give   [The words *will give* is in the future tense. Is this the correct form?]
    D gave   [The verb *gave* is in the past tense. Is this the correct form?]

Answer Key

 Chapter 1 Using Your
Writing Process

Reading Comprehension (page 1)

1. A   **2.** D

Developing Your Skills: Basic (pages 2–3)

RECOGNIZING FACT AND OPINION

1. A   **3.** A   **5.** A   **7.** A   **9.** A
2. A   **4.** B   **6.** B   **8.** B   **10.** B

CLARIFYING IDEAS

1–5 Responses will vary, but students should use the Venn diagram to compare and contrast what they think and what their parents think about the various topics.

Developing Your Skills: Intermediate (page 4)

RECOGNIZING FACTS

1. A   **3.** A   **5.** B   **7.** A   **9.** B
2. B   **4.** B   **6.** A   **8.** A   **10.** A

Developing Your Skills: Advanced (page 5)

SUPPORTING WITH FACTS

1–5 Answers will vary, but students should write opinions that are based on the facts presented in the exercise.

 Chapter 2 Developing Your
Writing Style

Reading Comprehension (page 6)

1. A   **2.** B

Developing Your Skills: Basic (pages 7–8)

IDENTIFYING SUPPORTING DETAILS

1. A   **3.** A   **5.** A   **7.** A   **9.** B
2. B   **4.** A   **6.** B   **8.** B   **10.** A

CLUSTERING

1–5 Responses will vary, but students should use the cluster diagrams to generate supporting details.

Developing Your Skills: Intermediate (page 9)

IDENTIFYING SUPPORTING DETAILS

1. A   **3.** B   **5.** B   **7.** A   **9.** A
2. A   **4.** A   **6.** B   **8.** A   **10.** A

Developing Your Skills: Advanced (page 10)

PROVIDING SUPPORTING DETAILS

1–5 Responses will vary but students should write supporting details that logically support the various sentences.

Chapter 3 Writing Informative
Paragraphs

Reading Comprehension (page 11)

1. B   **2.** A

Developing Your Skills: Basic (pages 12–13)

USING THE CORRECT WORD

1. A   **3.** A   **5.** A   **7.** A   **9.** B
2. B   **4.** A   **6.** A   **8.** B   **10.** A

WORD WEB

1–5 Responses will vary, but students should use the cluster diagrams to generate vivid words.

Developing Your Skills: Intermediate (page 14)

USING THE CORRECT WORD

1. A   **3.** A   **5.** A   **7.** A   **9.** A
2. B   **4.** B   **6.** A   **8.** B   **10.** B

Developing Your Skills: Advanced (page 15)

USING VIVID WORDS

1–5 Responses will vary, but students should replace the clichés with vivid and strong words.

Reading Comprehension *(page 18)*

1. A   **2.** A

Developing Your Skills: Basic *(pages 19–20)*

TRANSITION WORDS

1. B	**3.** A	**5.** B	**7.** A	**9.** A
2. B	**4.** A	**6.** A	**8.** B	**10.** A

CAUSE AND EFFECT
Answers will vary.

Developing Your Skills: Intermediate *(page 21)*

POINT OF VIEW

1. B	**3.** A	**5.** B	**7.** B	**9.** A
2. B	**4.** A	**6.** A	**8.** A	**10.** B

Developing Your Skills: Advanced *(page 22)*

DESCRIPTIVE PARAGRAPHS
1–5 Responses will vary but topic sentences should indicate the students' opinions on the topics.

 Chapter 5   Writing Effective Compositions

Reading Comprehension *(page 25)*

1. B   **2.** B

Developing Your Skills: Basic *(pages 26–27)*

DETERMINING THE MEANINGS OF WORDS

1. A	**3.** B	**5.** A	**7.** A	**9.** B
2. B	**4.** A	**6.** B	**8.** B	**10.** B

ADDING PREFIXES *(page 27)*
1–5 Comes before = predates; don't believe = disbelief; not enjoyable = unenjoyable; not trusting = distrustful; not enchanted = disenchanted

Developing Your Skills: Intermediate *(page 28)*

DETERMINING WORD MEANINGS

1. A	**3.** A	**5.** B	**7.** B	**9.** A
2. B	**4.** A	**6.** A	**8.** A	**10.** B

Developing Your Skills: Advanced *(page 29)*

DETERMINING THE MEANINGS OF WORDS
1–5 Responses will vary but students should write a separate sentence for each definition.

Chapter 6   Writing Effective Compositions

Reading Comprehension *(page 32)*

1. C   **2.** B

Developing Your Skills: Basic *(pages 33–34)*

DESCRIPTIVE, SENSORY AND BACKGROUND DETAILS

1. B	**3.** B	**5.** B	**7.** A	**9.** B
2. A	**4.** C	**6.** C	**8.** C	**10.** A

FINDING DETAILS *(page 34)*
1–5 Responses will vary but students should use the cluster diagrams to generate descriptive, sensory and background details.

Developing Your Skills: Intermediate *(page 35)*

CREATING VIVID IMAGES

1. A	**3.** A	**5.** B	**7.** A	**9.** A
2. B	**4.** A	**6.** A	**8.** B	**10.** B

Developing Your Skills: Advanced *(page 36)*

WRITING VIVID DETAILS
1–5 Responses will vary but students should create vivid details with the words provided.

Chapter 7   Using Description: Observation

Reading Comprehension *(page 39)*

1. D   **2.** B

Developing Your Skills: Basic *(pages 40–41)*

DESCRIPTIVE WRITING

1. A	**3.** B	**5.** A	**7.** B	**9.** B
2. B	**4.** A	**6.** A	**8.** B	**10.** A

SENSORY DIAGRAM
1–5 Responses will vary but students should use the organizers to generate vivid words.

Developing Your Skills: Intermediate (page 42)

USING FIGURATIVE LANGUAGE
1. A	**3.** B	**5.** A	**7.** B	**9.** A
2. A	**4.** A	**6.** A	**8.** A	**10.** B

Developing Your Skills: Advanced (page 43)

WRITING DESCRIPTIONS
USING FIGURATIVE LANGUAGE
1–5 Responses will vary but students should use figurative language.

Chapter 8 — Creative Writing: Stories, Plays, and Poems

Reading Comprehension (page 46)
1. A   **2.** A

Developing Your Skills: Basic (pages 47–48)

DESCRIPTIVE TOPIC SENTENCES
1. B	**3.** A	**5.** A	**7.** B	**9.** A
2. A	**4.** A	**6.** A	**8.** B	**10.** A

SKETCHING CHARACTERS
1–5 Responses will vary but students should complete the chart to describe the different character traits.

Developing Your Skills: Intermediate (page 49)

ORDERING EVENTS
1. B	**3.** B	**5.** A	**7.** A	**9.** A
2. A	**4.** A	**6.** B	**8.** B	**10.** B

Developing Your Skills: Advanced (page 50)

CHOOSING CHARACTER TRAITS
1–5 Responses will vary, but students should write four sentences describing a character trait for each character.

Chapter 9 — Writing to Inform and Explain

Reading Comprehension (page 53)
1. B   **2.** A

Developing Your Skills: Basic (pages 54–55)

STEPS IN A PROCESS
1. A	**3.** B	**5.** A	**7.** B	**9.** B
2. B	**4.** A	**6.** A	**8.** B	**10.** B

SENSORY DIAGRAM
1–5 Responses will vary, but students should use the pyramid to logically organize the information.

Developing Your Skills: Intermediate (page 56)

TYPES OF ORDER
1. A	**3.** A	**5.** A	**7.** A	**9.** A
2. B	**4.** A	**6.** B	**8.** A	**10.** B

Developing Your Skills: Advanced (page 57)

WRITING SENTENCE USING PRONOUNS
1–5 Answers will vary.

Chapter 10 — Writing to Persuade

Reading Comprehension (page 60)
1. D   **2.** A

Developing Your Skills: Basic (pages 61–62)

IDENTIFYING YOUR AUDIENCE
1. A	**3.** B	**5.** A	**7.** B	**9.** A
2. A	**4.** B	**6.** B	**8.** B	**10.** A

PROS AND CONS
1–5 Responses will vary but students should use the chart to list both the pros and cons of the topics.

Developing Your Skills: Intermediate (page 63)

IDENTIFYING YOUR AUDIENCE
1. C	**3.** A	**5.** B	**7.** A	**9.** B
2. B	**4.** A	**6.** C	**8.** B	**10.** A

Developing Your Skills: Advanced (page 64)

PERSUASIVE TOPIC SENTENCES
1–5 Responses will vary, but students should use persuasive language effectively.

Chapter 11 Writing About Literature

Reading Comprehension (page 67)

1. B   **2.** C

Developing Your Skills: Basic (pages 68–69)

GATHERING EVIDENCE

1. A	**3.** B	**5.** B	**7.** A	**9.** A
2. A	**4.** B	**6.** A	**8.** A	**10.** A

GATHERING EVIDENCE—WORD WEB
1–5 Responses will vary, but students should use word webs to generate ideas about each of the sentences.

Developing Your Skills: Intermediate (page 70)

GATHERING EVIDENCE

1. A	**3.** A	**5.** B	**7.** A	**9.** B
2. B	**4.** A	**6.** B	**8.** B	**10.** A

Developing Your Skills: Advanced (page 71)

GATHERING EVIDENCE
1–5 Answers will vary.

Chapter 12 Research Reports

Reading Comprehension (page 74)

1. D   **2.** D

Developing Your Skills: Basic (pages 75–76)

CHOOSING AND LIMITING A RESEARCH SUBJECT

1. B	**3.** A	**5.** A	**7.** B	**9.** B
2. A	**4.** B	**6.** A	**8.** A	**10.** B

CLAUSES
1–5 Answers will vary.

Developing Your Skills: Intermediate (page 77)

WORKS CITED PAGE

1. B	**3.** A	**5.** B	**7.** B	**9.** A
2. A	**4.** B	**6.** A	**8.** B	**10.** A

Developing Your Skills: Advanced (page 78)

LIMITING A RESEARCH SUBJECT AND DEVELOPING A THESIS
1–5 Responses will vary but students should write thesis statements for limited subjects.

Chapter 13 Letters and Applications

Reading Comprehension (page 81)

1. A   **2.** A

Developing Your Skills: Basic (pages 82–83)

WRITING LETTERS

1. A	**3.** B	**5.** B	**7.** A	**9.** B
2. B	**4.** A	**6.** A	**8.** B	**10.** A

WRITING LETTERS
1. business letter
2. business letter
3. personal letter
4. personal letter
5. personal letter

Developing Your Skills: Intermediate (page 84)

BUSINESS LETTERS

1. B	**3.** B	**5.** A	**7.** B	**9.** A
2. A	**4.** A	**6.** B	**8.** A	**10.** B

Developing Your Skills: Advanced (page 85)

WRITING LETTERS
1. 1704 Milton Manor
Springfield, CA 90210
2. Mr. Gary Scraves
Maps Unlimited
1528 Montgomery Street
Seattle, WA 98141
3. Sincerely,
Betty Smith
4. March 11, 2000

5. 1421 Dere Road, Apartment 2C
Jersey City, New Jersey

Chapter 14   Speeches, Presentations, and Discussions

Reading Comprehension *(page 86)*
1. A   **2.** A

Developing Your Skills: Basic *(pages 87–88)*

CHOOSING AND LIMITING A SUBJECT

1. A	**3.** B	**5.** B	**7.** B	**9.** B
2. A	**4.** A	**6.** A	**8.** B	**10.** A

STRATEGIES FOR LISTENING—CHART
1. verbal
2. verbal
3. nonverbal
4. nonverbal
5. verbal

Developing Your Skills: Intermediate *(page 89)*

STRATEGIES FOR LISTENING— RECOGNIZING APPEALS

1. A	**3.** A	**5.** B	**7.** A	**9.** A
2. B	**4.** C	**6.** A	**8.** B	**10.** C

Developing Your Skills: Advanced *(page 90)*

STRATEGIES FOR LISTENING— GLITTERING GENERALITIES
1–5 Responses will vary.

LANGUAGE

Chapter 1   The Sentence

B. Language Skills *(page 94)*
1. B   **2.** A   **3.** C   **4.** B

C. Language Skills *(page 94)*

BASIC	INTERMEDIATE	ADVANCED
1. C	**4.** A	**7.** B
2. B	**5.** C	**8.** A
3. A	**6.** C	**9.** C

Chapter 2   Nouns and Pronouns

B. Language Skills *(page 97)*
1. B   **2.** A   **3.** C   **4.** B

C. Language Skills *(page 97)*

BASIC	INTERMEDIATE	ADVANCED
1. C	**4.** A	**7.** B
2. B	**5.** C	**8.** A
3. A	**6.** C	**9.** C

Chapter 3   Verbs

B. Language Skills *(page 100)*
1. B   **2.** A   **3.** C   **4.** B

C. Language Skills *(page 100)*

BASIC	INTERMEDIATE	ADVANCED
1. C	**4.** A	**7.** B
2. B	**5.** C	**8.** A
3. A	**6.** C	**9.** C

Chapter 4   Adjectives and Adverbs

B. Language Skills *(page 103)*
1. B   **2.** A   **3.** B   **4.** C

C. Language Skills *(page 103)*

BASIC	INTERMEDIATE	ADVANCED
1. C	**4.** A	**7.** B
2. B	**5.** C	**8.** A
3. A	**6.** C	**9.** C

Chapter 5   Other Parts of Speech

B. Language Skills *(page 106)*
1. B   **2.** A   **3.** C   **4.** B

C. Language Skills *(page 106)*

BASIC	INTERMEDIATE	ADVANCED
1. C	**4.** A	**7.** B
2. B	**5.** C	**8.** A
3. A	**6.** C	**9.** A

Chapter 6   Complements

B. Language Skills *(page 109)*

1. B	2. A	3. C	4. A

C. Language Skills *(page 109)*

BASIC	INTERMEDIATE	ADVANCED
1. C	4. A	7. B
2. B	5. C	8. A
3. A	6. C	9. C

Chapter 7   Phrases

B. Language Skills *(page 112)*

1. B	2. A	3. C	4. B

C. Language Skills *(page 112)*

BASIC	INTERMEDIATE	ADVANCED
1. C	4. A	7. A
2. B	5. C	8. A
3. A	6. C	9. B

Chapter 8   Clauses

B. Language Skills *(page 115)*

1. A	2. B	3. C	4. B

C. Language Skills *(page 115)*

BASIC	INTERMEDIATE	ADVANCED
1. C	3. A	5. A
2. B	4. C	6. C

Chapter 9   Sentence Fragments and Run-ons

B. Language Skills *(page 118)*

1. B	2. A	3. C	4. C

C. Language Skills *(page 118)*

BASIC	INTERMEDIATE	ADVANCED
1. C	3. A	5. B
2. B	4. C	

Chapter 10   Using Verbs

B. Language Skills *(page 121)*

1. B	2. A	3. C	4. A

C. Language Skills *(page 121)*

BASIC	INTERMEDIATE	ADVANCED
1. A	4. C	7. A
2. C	5. B	8. C
3. C	6. C	9. C

Chapter 11   Using Pronouns

B. Language Skills *(page 124)*

1. C	2. A	3. C	4. B

C. Language Skills *(page 124)*

BASIC	INTERMEDIATE	ADVANCED
1. C	4. A	7. B
2. B	5. B	8. C
3. A	6. C	9. A

Chapter 12   Subject and Verb Agreement

B. Language Skills *(page 127)*

1. A	2. B	3. B	4. C

C. Language Skills *(page 127)*

BASIC	INTERMEDIATE	ADVANCED
1. B	4. A	7. A
2. C	5. C	8. B
3. B	6. C	9. B

Chapter 13   Using Adjectives and Adverbs

B. Language Skills *(page 130)*

1. A	2. C	3. B	4. C

C. Language Skills *(page 130)*

BASIC	INTERMEDIATE	ADVANCED
1. A	4. A	7. C
2. C	5. B	8. B
3. B	6. C	9. C

Chapter 14   Capital Letters

B. Language Skills *(page 133)*

1. B   **2.** C   **3.** C   **4.** C

C. Language Skills *(page 133)*

BASIC	INTERMEDIATE	ADVANCED
1. B	**4.** B	**7.** C
2. C	**5.** A	**8.** C
3. C	**6.** C	

Chapter 15   End Marks and Commas

B. Language Skills *(page 136)*

1. B   **2.** C   **3.** B   **4.** C

C. Language Skills *(page 136)*

BASIC	INTERMEDIATE	ADVANCED
1. A	**4.** B	**7.** B
2. D	**5.** B	**8.** B
3. C	**6.** B	

Chapter 16   Italics and Quotation Marks

B. Language Skills *(page 139)*

1. B   **2.** A   **3.** C   **4.** C

C. Language Skills *(page 139)*

BASIC	INTERMEDIATE	ADVANCED
1. B	**3.** A	**5.** B
2. C	**4.** A	**6.** C

Chapter 17   Other Punctuation

B. Language Skills *(page 142)*

1. C   **2.** C   **3.** B   **4.** A

C. Language Skills *(page 142)*

BASIC	INTERMEDIATE	ADVANCED
1. C	**3.** C	**5.** A
2. A	**4.** C	**6.** C

UNIT 1

What to Do If You See a Bear

Guided Reading *(page 145)*

1. C   **2.** D   **3.** C   **4.** B

Composition *(page 146)*

Responses will vary, but essays should include facts and examples that support opinions and that are organized in logical order.

Editing *(page 147)*

1. A   **2.** C   **3.** C   **4.** B

UNIT 2

Sherman Alexie's "This is What It Means to Say Phoenix, Arizona"

Guided Reading *(page 149)*

1. D   **2.** C   **3.** A   **4.** C

Composition *(page 150)*

Responses will vary but should include supporting details that are organized in a logical order, such as compare-and-contrast order.

Editing *(page 151)*

1. A   **2.** C   **3.** B   **4.** D

UNIT 3

When Squids Attack

Guided Reading *(page 153)*

1. D   **2.** B   **3.** B   **4.** B

Composition *(page 154)*

Responses will vary but should include supporting details that are organized in a logical order, such as order of importance or compare-and-contrast order.

Editing *(page 155)*

1. A   **2.** B   **3.** B   **4.** D

UNIT 4

You Call This a Vacation?

Guided Reading *(page 157)*

1. C   **2.** C   **3.** A   **4.** C

Composition *(page 158)*

Responses will vary, but supporting details should be ordered in a logical order, such as chronological, sequential, or cause-and-effect order.

Editing *(page 159)*

1. A   **2.** C   **3.** C   **4.** D

UNIT 5

Fortitudine Vincimus— By Endurance We Conquer

Guided Reading *(page 161)*

1. D   **2.** A   **3.** A   **4.** D

Composition *(page 162)*

Responses will vary, but support details should be organized in a logical order, such as order of importance or cause-and-effect order.

Editing *(page 163)*

1. B   **2.** A   **3.** A   **4.** C

UNIT 6

Sports Heroes Deserve High Salaries; What's Up With Sports Salaries?

Guided Reading *(page 165)*

1. B   **2.** A   **3.** A

Composition *(page 166)*

Responses will vary, but essays should include facts and examples to support opinions. Supporting details should be organized in logical order, such as order of importance or cause-and-effect order.

Editing *(page 167)*

1. B   **2.** A   **3.** D   **4.** D

UNIT 7

New York, New York

Guided Reading *(page 169)*

1. A   **2.** C   **3.** A   **4.** A

Composition *(page 170)*

Responses will vary, but essays should include vivid details that are organized in a logical order.

Editing *(page 171)*

1. B   **2.** C   **3.** A   **4.** B

UNIT 8

An American Original

Guided Reading *(page 173)*

1. A   **2.** A   **3.** C   **4.** B

Composition *(page 174)*

Responses will vary but should include facts and examples to support opinions.

Editing *(page 175)*

1. B   **2.** A   **3.** A   **4.** D